SMALL WORLD INITIATIVE

A Research Guide to Microbial and Chemical Diversity
Fourth Edition

Simon Hernandez

Tiffany Tsang

Carol Bascom-Slack

Jo Handelsman

Edited by

Nichole Broderick

Erika Kurt

Small World Initiative Press
crowdsourcing antibiotic discovery

XanEdu
Change the course.

SWI Research Protocols and Guide Bundle ISBN: 978-1-50669-699-7
Component 1 *SWI A Research Guide to Microbial and Chemical Diversity* ISBN: 978-1-50669-698-0

Authors: Simon Hernandez, Tiffany Tsang, Carol Bascom-Slack, Jo Handelsman
Editors: Nichole Broderick, Erika Kurt
Cover Art: Sarah Jeon, McGill University, 2015.

Terms of Use and Disclaimer

XanEdu
Change the course.

530 Great Road
Acton, MA 01720
800-562-2147
www.xanedu.com

Contents

Acknowledgments

We thank all the talented and creative people who contributed to Small World Initiative: A Research Guide to Microbial and Chemical Diversity and Small World Initiative: Research Protocols. This version of the guide and protocols is the product of years of writing, testing, and refining by very dedicated people.

We would like to thank Yale's Center for Scientific Teaching for supporting our writers, editors, and partners through this process. The Center helped steer us toward the collaborative efforts that have brought this resource together. We thank the National Institutes of Health's National Biosafety and Biocontainment Training Program for helping to keep our students safe through their review of our biosafety protocols that ensure that we are recommending best practices and our 2015-2016 Science Committee Co-Chairs Samantha Gruenheid from McGill University and Kristen Butela from Seton Hill University for their valuable contributions to these safety efforts. We are grateful to the American Society for Microbiology (ASM) for providing guidance and resources. The spread and streak plate protocols are being used with ASM's permission and were originally published as part of ASM Microbe Library Laboratory Protocols (http://www.asmscience.org/content/education/protocol).

A special thanks to Michelle Legaspi from Yale's Molecular, Biophysics and Biochemistry Department for her critical eye and copy-editing skills and to Gillian Phillips for her chemistry advice. Thanks to all of the Small World Initiative Pilot Partners for their thoughtful feedback and helpful suggestions, but especially Todd Kelson, one of our original pilot partners from Brigham Young University who served as program coordinator 2014-2015, and to other partners whose contributions have transformed this text: Sachie Etherington from the University of Hawaii, Michael Buckholt from Worcester Polytechnic University, Erica Suchman from Colorado State University, Barbara Murdoch from Eastern Connecticut State University, Ann Buchmann from Chadron State College, Ana Barral from National University, Jean Schmidt from University of Pittsburgh, Karen Pelletreau from University of Connecticut, and Neil Enis from Tulsa Community College. We are also grateful to those who have taught with us, in particular, Jessamina Blum and Gabriel Lozano.

We thank Howard Hughes Medical Institute Professors Graham Hatfull, Sally Elgin, and Scott Strobel for inspiring us with their brilliant research courses and their assessment of student impacts and for advising us in development of the Small World Initiative. And finally, we thank all of our students who have participated in this endeavor in its fledgling years and who helped it mature to the worldwide network it has become.

Small World Initiative™ Overview

"**Fewer than 40%** of college students intending to major in STEM fields complete a STEM degree...[many citing] **uninspiring introductory courses** as a factor in their choice to switch majors."

President's Council of Advisors on Science and Technology

Antibiotic resistance is "**the greatest and most urgent global risk.**"

United Nations

This guide is part of the official materials used in the Small World Initiative™ (SWI). Formulated at Yale University in 2012 by the author, Dr. Jo Handelsman, SWI is an innovative program that inspires and retains students in the sciences while addressing a worldwide health threat – the diminishing supply of effective antibiotics. SWI centers around a discovery-based introductory biology course in which students from around the world perform hands-on field and laboratory research on soil samples in the hunt for new antibiotics. This is particularly relevant since over two thirds of antibiotics originate from soil bacteria or fungi.

Differentiating itself from traditional courses, SWI's biology course provides original research opportunities rather than relying on cookbook experiments with predetermined results. Through a series of student-driven experiments, students collect soil samples, isolate diverse bacteria, test their bacteria against clinically relevant microorganisms, and characterize those showing inhibitory activity. SWI's approach also provides a platform to crowdsource antibiotic discovery by tapping into the intellectual power of many student researchers concurrently addressing a global challenge and advances promising candidates into the drug development pipeline. This unique class approach harnesses the power of active learning to achieve both educational and scientific goals.

Over the past four years, SWI has grown rapidly to include 167 participating schools across 35 US states, Puerto Rico, and 12 countries. The program seeks to inspire the next generation of Partner Instructors and collaborators who will pledge to further SWI's mission to transform science education and promote antibiotic discovery through the curiosity and creativity of young scientists around the world. SWI's Partner Instructors are committed to making meaningful and measurable improvements in the education landscape and expanding opportunities for their students while addressing real-world health challenges. If you are interested in learning more about the Small World Initiative, please visit www.smallworldinitiative.org.

Small World Initiative™ Community

The community aspects of the Small World Initiative make up the backbone of this collaborative endeavor. We strongly encourage you to participate in the broader SWI community and to take advantage of these unique opportunities.

Social Media/Blog

This is a great way to connect with the broader SWI community and learn about upcoming opportunities.

Facebook Group – The "Small World Initiative: Global Community" group is SWI's most popular way for students and faculty to informally connect and learn about community activities.

Twitter – @Team_SWI

Instagram – team_swi

YouTube – Small World Initiative – You may find and upload helpful videos here.

Blog – SWI's blog is the most visited part of the website. If you have a great idea, make an interesting discovery, or just want to share your experience, we want to hear from you!

Data Collection – www.smallworldinitiative.org/data

We collect several tiers of data to report on SWI's impact and to assist in achieving SWI's educational and scientific goals. Data collection tools are provided on SWI's website. In particular, we ask you to create an account and upload detailed information on your soil samples to SWI's **Soil Sample Database**. In addition to serving as a recorded account of your research, this information will be invaluable for our screening laboratory and for continued research. Don't let your important research results go unnoticed. Record your data in our online database!

Annual Symposium

Each year, SWI Partner Instructors and students gather at our Annual Symposium to present their original research. Past Symposia have been held in conjunction with the American Society for Microbiology and provide the opportunity to build relationships within the SWI community, present scientific and pedagogical research to experts, and explore science careers. Consider presenting your research and meeting fellow scientists.

Awards

Each year, we give out awards designed to further SWI's educational and scientific goals, and we have an annual call for nominations from students and faculty.

Student Awards:

- Excellence in Scientific Persistence Award
- Best-in-Session Student Poster Award
- Excellence in Leadership Award
- Excellence in Scientific Discovery Award

Faculty Awards:

- Joseph P. Caruso Award for Excellence in Mentorship
- Excellence in Scientific Discovery Award
- Excellence in Pedagogical Innovation Award

Open Awards:

- SWI Support Person of the Year Award
- External Supporter Awards

Periodically, we also give out travel awards to SWI's Annual Symposium and host other contests. Please consider nominating your peers and instructors for these awards.

Opportunities Portal

We curate a database of opportunities exclusively for SWI Partner Instructors, current SWI students, and SWI alums on SWI's website. This includes relevant conferences, speaking and writing opportunities, internships, fellowships, and jobs. Password: treats4swi. As the password may be changed, we recommend subscribing to receive the opportunities digest.

Other Annual Events

Each year, we encourage faculty and students to reach out to their communities to spread the word on the antibiotic crisis and other science- and health-related issues. For example, for Antibiotic Awareness Week in November, we ask schools to host an event that may involve anything from a film screening or open house lab to a color run or antibiotic-themed bake sale. Please consider how you may wish to participate.

Introduction: The Antibiotic Crisis

There is a crisis brewing in the world with untold health, economic, and political consequences. We are on the precipice of entering a post-antibiotic era, when a scraped knee or common infection may prove deadly for an otherwise healthy individual. Because of antimicrobial resistance (AMR), common and life-threatening infections are increasingly becoming untreatable. AMR occurs when microorganisms, such as bacteria, viruses, fungi, and parasites, change in ways that render the medications used to cure the infections they cause ineffective. When this happens, they are often referred to colloquially as **superbugs**. This proliferation of superbugs is being seen worldwide. There is a silent epidemic of multidrug-resistant typhoid raging across Africa and Asia, killing 200,000 each year; multidrug-resistant tuberculosis (MDR-TB) has been identified in 105 countries; and the US Centers for Disease Control and Prevention (CDC) announced that more than 800,000 Americans may soon be at risk of acquiring untreatable gonorrhea each year (CDC, 2016).

With the growing problem of AMR, even routine medical procedures could prove too risky to undergo. While you reminisce of days when you could take a weeklong course of antibiotics to cure an infection, you may soon find yourself lucky if you are prescribed a treatment with a 50% cure rate that takes two years, hundreds of injections, and 14,000 pills, which is already the case for more than 500,000 suffering from MDR-TB. According to the World Health Organization (WHO) Director General, Margaret Chan, "Doctors facing patients will increasingly have to say, 'I am sorry. There is nothing I can do for you.'"

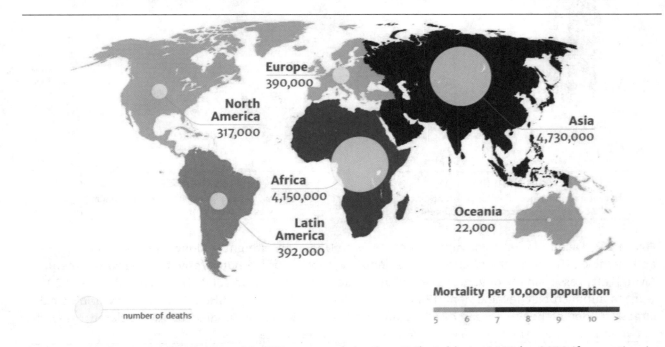

Figure 0-1. The Cost of Inaction – 10 million annual deaths attributable to AMR by 2050 if no action is taken. Image source: Review on Antimicrobial Resistance.

AMR and the resulting diminishing supply of effective antibiotics are two of the biggest threats to global health today. This is no surprise. Even Alexander Fleming, who discovered penicillin, the world's first antibiotic, warned of the danger of resistance. Each year in the US alone, there are more than 2 million AMR illnesses, 23,000 deaths, and $35 billion in economic losses (CDC, 2015). Globally, there are more than 700,000 AMR deaths annually (WHO, 2016). According to an often-cited analysis from the Review on Antimicrobial Resistance, if no action is taken between now and 2050, the true cost of AMR will be 300 million premature deaths, killing more people than cancer and diabetes combined, and $100 trillion in terms of global Gross Domestic Product (GDP).

Yet while existing antibiotics are losing efficacy due to widespread resistance, the pace of antibiotic discovery is not keeping up with the rapid evolution of resistance in microbes. Many of the major pharmaceutical companies that had driven the antibiotic discovery process have eliminated or reduced their discovery programs in favor of developing more lucrative drugs. As a result, there has been more than a 30-year void in discovery of new types of antibiotics with no registered classes of antibiotics discovered after the 1980s (Pew Charitable Trusts, 2016). So while the crisis escalates, the commitment to drug development is decreasing.

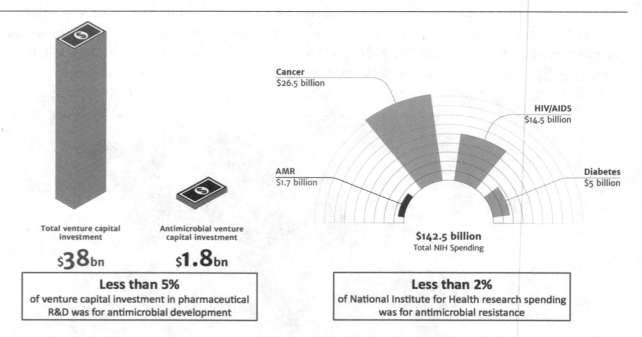

Figure 0-2. Failed Market Dynamics & Public/Private Under-Investment – Along with the divestment in antimicrobial R&D from the pharmaceutical industry, there is broad public/private under-investment in AMR. **[Left]** Less than 5% of venture capital investment in pharmaceutical R&D between 2003 and 2013 went to antimicrobial development. **[Right]** The US National Institutes of Health (NIH), the world's single largest funder of health research, allocated just 1.2% of its grant funding to AMR-related research between 2009 and 2014. Image source: Review on Antimicrobial Resistance.

Solutions – You Have a Very Important Role to Play

Although we are running out of time on one of the most pressing global challenges, we possess the ingenuity to solve this problem, and we already understand the key causes and many of the possible solutions. It is not too late if we respond effectively with global collaboration. While global action is required to solve this problem, you have a very important role to play in stemming AMR.

We are calling on you to use antibiotics correctly, take action to prevent the spread of infectious diseases, and multiply your efforts by spreading the word. While AMR occurs naturally through processes discussed in Section 10, there are several factors that drastically accelerate this process. By far, the primary cause of AMR is the mass-scale misuse and overuse of antibiotics in agriculture and humans. Other factors include poor prevention and control of infections related to inadequate sanitation, hygiene, vaccine rates, surveillance, and diagnostics.

In addition to using antibiotics correctly and reducing the spread of infectious diseases, we need to find new drugs to treat antibiotic-resistant infections, and we are calling on you to join us in this endeavor. One of the most promising approaches to finding new antibiotics is through mass-scale fundamental biological discovery. Through your research efforts in this course, you are joining a global collaborative effort to discover new antibiotics.

How do we identify new drugs?

Microbes living in the soil are the source of the vast majority of antibiotic compounds on the market today. It may seem odd that the class of organisms intended as the target of antibacterial compounds is also a source of new antibiotics. Much remains to be learned about why soil microbes produce antibiotics and what conditions trigger production, but we know that a small percentage of the total number of soil microbes *do* produce inhibitory compounds under laboratory conditions. The key lies in identifying those valuable microbes. Our estimates indicate that there are likely 4,000 to 40,000 species per gram of soil (Schloss & Handelsman, 2006); others have placed this estimate in the millions (Gans *et al.*, 2005). Whatever the exact number, there is no question that soils worldwide contain a massive collective resource. Since soil bacteria has proven a rich source of drug-like compounds, continuing this exploration on a massive scale presents a unique opportunity for drug discovery.

Can a team of eager student researchers solve the antibiotic crisis?

The answer is a resounding, "Yes!" One potential obstacle in the identification and development of novel antibiotics is that pharmaceutical companies have calculated that the probability of identifying a novel compound is too low to be worth investment. The "low-hanging fruit," so to speak, has been picked. In addition, drugs that are prescribed for chronic conditions, such as anxiety, depression, heart disease, and elevated cholesterol, are more profitable than antibiotics that are prescribed for a relatively short duration. While antibiotic discovery and development is not a semester-long process, we can certainly make headway in identifying potential candidates in a few months – and learn about the research process along the way. By harnessing the power of many student researchers, we can extend the discovery process to a wide range of geographic locations and a worldwide community of volunteers where every individual has the potential to make novel discoveries. In addition, the sum of our collective results will be informative and could help advance science in new and interesting ways, regardless of the outcome in terms of antibiotic production. Database entries from around the world will help to identify trends in microbes that produce antibiotics and will help to delineate environmental areas where antibiotic resistance is prevalent among soil microbes. Science today is usually a collaborative effort by individuals in many laboratories and is advanced over time through the successive efforts of many. The goal of the Small World Initiative is to create a global community of student researchers, working together to solve the antibiotic crisis through the discovery of novel antibiotic-producing bacteria.

References

Antibiotic Resistance Threats in the United States, U.S. Department of Health and Human Services, Centers for Disease Control and Prevention (2013).

Gans, J., Woilinsky M., Dunbar, J. (2005). Computational improvements reveal great bacterial diversity and high metal toxicity in soil. Science 309:1387-1390.

Meeting the Challenge of Antimicrobial Resistance, World Health Organization (2016), http://www.who.int/life-course/news/events/antimicrobial-resistance-report/en/.

Schloss, P. D., Handelsman, J. (2006). Toward a census of bacteria in soil. PLOS Computational Biology 2:786-793.

A Scientific Roadmap for Antibiotic Discovery, The Pew Charitable Trusts (2016), http://www.pewtrusts.org/~/media/assets/2016/05/ascientificroadmapforantibioticdiscovery.pdf.

Spellberg, B., Powers, J. H., Brass, E. P., Miller, L. G., Edwards, J. E., Jr. (2004). Trends in antimicrobial drug development: implications for the future. Clin Infect Dis 38:1279-1286 doi: 10.1086/420937 pmid: 15127341.

How to Use This Research Guide

This *Research Guide* is designed to provide background information for each experiment in your research project. As a student researcher, you will be tasked with formulating your own hypotheses, designing your own experiments, picking which protocols to use, and interpreting and presenting your findings. As with every authentic research project, you will not have all the answers upfront. This *Research Guide* is not meant to give you a set of instructions on how to execute your experiment or tell you everything you need to know about the subject. Instead, it will provide you with general **concepts**, **principles**, and **prompts** to *guide* you through the project.

Concepts

The **concepts** include a small selection of general biological and microbiological information, brief descriptions of what you would normally find in your textbook and gain from the lecture portion of your course in greater detail. This *Research Guide* and your traditional course materials (e.g., textbooks, lecture slides and notes, and content of class discussions and exercises) are meant to complement each other and should be used simultaneously. By reading each section, we will give you enough information to get you thinking about the topic at hand and give you a basis to pursue more information in your course materials. Use this opportunity to pursue information in a more targeted and goal-oriented manner. Ask yourself, what else would be relevant to know for this experiment or to answer the biological questions? By doing so, you will start to think like a researcher and take ownership of your research.

Principles

The **principles** are general microbiological guidelines to perform your experiments. We will provide you with some examples of microbiological techniques to show you some of the traditional approaches to answer the biological questions. The *Research Protocols* contain an assortment of traditional microbiological and Small World Initiative protocols. After reading each section, you will be prompted to pick a protocol from the list. In some cases, your instructor will provide additional protocols, or you will be asked to design your own or find one in the literature. While some experiments have well-established protocols associated with them, which would yield the best results, you must always determine what you are trying to accomplish with your experiment and what your idea of "best results" is. Always come up with a set of criteria and definitions to be consistent in your work. Maybe you disagree with the traditional approach and can think of alternative ways to address the experiment and obtain even better results. We encourage this evaluation process because it will give you the critical thinking skills to execute any type of research. Moreover, it will give you more insights as a scientist and make you more knowledgeable of the scientific method.

Prompts

Finally, this *Research Guide* will feature a variety of **prompts**. These prompts will be scattered in the section reading or come in the form of Biological Questions or Experiment prompts. At the end of every section, you will come across the topic or the goal of the experiment at the heading and the Biological Questions below it. This is where the *guiding* part of the *Research Guide* comes in. With every phenomenon we want to understand, or issue we wish to address, we will come up with a list of questions. *Why is the sky blue? How will I solve world hunger? What is the matter with dung beetles?* We have come up with some of the main questions for you, which should be evident after reading the background information in the section and browsing through some of your course materials. Use these questions to make informed hypotheses and design your experiments with specific outcomes in mind. The prompts will encompass the premise and the objective of the experiment, but you must tease those things apart yourself to start thinking like a scientist and own your project. With every experiment, you will need to answer prompts, which are necessary to keep track of and record your research as well as validate your scientific approach and your findings. Should you need more room to write answers than what is provided (you probably will), use your own lab notebook. The following prompts are examples of the main anatomy of the Experimental Sheet at the end of every section:

- **Background:** What led to the biological questions at hand? What is the issue or the phenomenon you want to learn more about?
- **Objective:** List the objective(s) of the experiment. What do you wish to learn about the issues or phenomena at hand?
- **Hypothesis:** Come with a temporary answer to your question and propose an outcome for your experiment. What do you propose is the explanation for the issue or the phenomenon at hand?
- **Experimental design:** Use text and graphics to explain your scientific approach. How will you go about testing your hypothesis?
- **Techniques/protocols used:** List the protocols you will refer to in the *Protocols* section, or a detailed description of alternative protocols (designed by you, provided by your instructor, or acquired from the literature). If you make any modification to the *Small World Initiative: Research Protocols*, make sure you list them here.
- **Results:** Describe the findings of your experiment. What observations did you make? What data did you collect? Do not leave out your negative results.
- **Interpretations**: What do your results mean? Speculate as to why you obtained the results you did, referring back to the original question and hypothesis. This will be the place to describe similar trends in your class results or the literature and come up with insights about what your results tell you. This will also be the place to reevaluate your hypothesis and come up with future directions.
- **Conclusion:** Wrap up your experiment with a brief summary and some of the new things you learned.

Use this resource to guide you through the research project and capture your sense of inquiry, observation, critical thinking, problem solving, and creativity. This is a guide into unchartered territory, and only you will be the expert on your findings. Enjoy the ride!

Section 1: Living on a Bacterial Planet

Microbes and the Environment

Microbes live in diverse natural habitats, ranging from hot hydrothermal vents deep in the ocean, to the insides of our guts and the surfaces of our computer keyboards. The ubiquity and versatility of microbes is the result of a long, intimate relationship between them and our planet, dating back nearly four billion years. Throughout this long journey, microbes have not been passive passengers but active contributors to the transformation of our planet and evolution of its inhabitants. They have shaped the biosphere, leading the evolution of complex cells and multicellular organisms that continue to be largely dependent on the specialized molecules and chemical products made by bacteria. Furthermore, microbes have and continue to greatly impact Earth's biogeochemical systems, driving the cycling of elements that would otherwise be inaccessible to other systems and organisms. Elements, such as carbon and nitrogen, would only exist in forms we cannot assimilate into our bodies without them. Microbes even play a large role in forming water droplets that produce rain in clouds and contribute to the formation of Earth's protective ozone layer.

Microbial ecology is the study of microbes' interactions with each other and with their respective environments. Microbes are part of complex ecosystems, and the communities within those ecosystems teem with life and bustle with activity. Microbes communicate, exchanging and sharing instructions to make new compounds. They may compete for limited resources or cooperate to maximize the availability of another. Two major focuses of microbial ecology relate to the **biodiversity** and **bioactivity** present in an ecosystem. These terms refer to the types of organisms present in an ecosystem and what their activities entail, respectively.

Definitions

Microbe is a general term for an organism that cannot be seen with the naked eye, or that is microscopic. Microbes include **prokaryotes** (i.e., **bacteria** and **archaea**) and microscopic **eukaryotes**, such as yeasts, molds, and protists. **Viruses** and **prions** are also lumped into the broad category of microbes. However, these agents do not meet all the basic requirements for life, such as the ability to reproduce on their own, and are therefore considered nonliving. Prokaryotes and eukaryotes differ in their level of complexity and cellular organization. Eukaryotes package their genetic material inside a compartment called the **nucleus,** whereas prokaryotes do not. Prokaryotes do not contain any intracellular compartments and have their genetic material in the cytoplasm.

Living on a Bacterial Planet.

The number of individual prokaryotic cells in soil across the planet has been estimated to be 26×10^{28} (260 billion billion billion) (Whitman, Coleman, & Wiebe, 1998). The collective impact of prokaryotes, such as bacteria, on our planet cannot be overstated.

This course will focus primarily on bacteria because:

- *Bacteria are virtually everywhere on the planet and are highly abundant – in many ways we live on a bacterial planet;*
- *Bacteria are great research tools because, in comparison with other organisms, they are simple but highly adapted to their environments and make specialized chemical compounds, many of which have human applications; and*
- *Bacteria greatly impact our health – some may cause infectious disease while others protect our bodies from invasion by harmful bacteria.*

Getting Started

In the Small World Initiative, we will conduct research involving soil bacteria and ask questions, many questions, pertaining to microbial ecology, such as:

- *What types of bacteria are present in our soil samples?*
- *How can we accurately count bacteria and tell them apart from one another?*
- *How many different types and/or individual bacteria of a given type are there?*
- *How do environmental factors influence these numbers?*
- *Does isolation influence bacterial activity?*
- *Are the activities of a particular bacterium beneficial or harmful to another bacterium?*
- *Do they produce specialized molecules like pigments, toxins, or antibiotics?*
- *How active are their antibiotics and what do they target?*
- *Are they resistant to the effects of other antibiotics?*
- *Can we manipulate their production of antibiotics?*
- *Are these antibiotics applicable to humans?*
- *Are they known or novel antibiotics?*

We will design and execute experiments to answer these questions, test hypotheses, and develop new insight into the microbial world. As microbiologists, we will refer to many disciplines in the natural sciences, ranging from cell biology and biochemistry to analytical chemistry and genetics. Tools developed in these disciplines will be very important for us over the following weeks as we assess the biodiversity and bioactivity present in our soil samples. We will be challenged to think critically about microbial interactions and functions as well as about ways that we can apply our newly acquired knowledge to enriching the existing body of knowledge and improving human welfare.

References

Whitman, W. B., Coleman, D. C., & Wiebe, W. J. (1998). Prokaryotes: the unseen majority. Proc Natl Acad Sci U S A, 95:6578-6583.

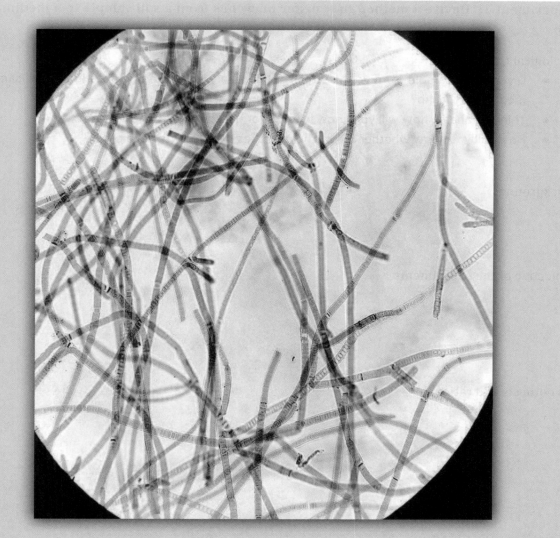

Living on a Bacterial Planet

This photo, taken through a light microscope eyepiece, shows the unique shape and color of the **photosynthetic cyanobacteria** (also known as blue-green algae). Cells form long chains (filaments) and inhabit a variety of habitats, including soil and oceans. Cyanobacteria produce oxygen through photosynthesis and also chemically modify gaseous nitrogen from the atmosphere, which they use for growth. The evolution of cyanobacteria 2.5 billion year ago was perhaps the most transformative event in Earth's evolutionary history. Massive amounts of oxygen were released into our planet's atmosphere for the first time, drastically changing its composition. This event triggered the mass extinction of many oxygen-sensitive microorganisms, enabled the evolution of oxygen-dependent respiration, and gave rise to the ozone layer, which allowed life to migrate to land and evolve into the wide biodiversity (the human species included) we see on Earth today.

Photo source: <u>commons.wikimedia.org</u> (public domain).

Experiment 1: Devise a method to transfer microbes from a soil sample to a medium in the lab

Biological Questions:
- Given a soil sample from your instructor, how can you isolate microbes in the soil sample to a medium in the lab?
- Thinking ahead, how will you know whether or not the microbes are living?
- How will you know whether or not the microbes interact with each other?

Background:

Objective of the experiment:

Hypothesis and rationale:

Isolation method used:

Observations:

Evaluation and conclusions:

Notes:

Section 2: More Than Just "Dirt"

Soil

Throughout human history, humans have looked at soil with a sense of mysticism and spirituality, in appreciation for its necessity for life. Soil sustains humans through agriculture and provides a platform for our daily activities. In many respects, soil not only sustains us but also makes us who we are. The development of civilizations has depended on soil health; poor soils have resulted in the collapse of entire civilizations, whereas fertile soils have enabled civilizations to flourish. As a symbol of fertility and the raw materials of life, soil has inspired many of the world's religions and traditions.

Soil is an extensive natural body covering most of Earth's terrestrial surface and mediating Earth's systems in the biosphere, atmosphere, hydrosphere, and lithosphere. Most evident of all, soil supports forests and plant life, which in turn produces half of the oxygen in the atmosphere and 95% of the world's food. Soil greatly influences the planet's ecosystems but is itself affected by natural forces and human, or anthropogenic, activities as well. Humans extract large quantities of soil constituents that have accumulated over millions of years through weathering and sedimentation. Human activity can disrupt the natural cycling of elements and can pollute the soil with extraneous chemicals that natural ecosystems are not well suited to remove or degrade. All these external factors greatly influence the life that depends on soil and can produce predictable changes in the degrees of biodiversity, bioactivity, and biomass we observe. This is because soil is itself an ecosystem for some of the most numerous, diverse, and dynamic organisms on Earth.

Soil Characteristics

The main characteristics defining soil are its physical structure, chemical composition, and association with plant roots or other resident organisms. The association of soil with plant roots creates a distinction between soil types that is often referenced by microbiologists and agronomists. We can distinguish between the **rhizosphere**, or soil that is in direct contact with living plant roots and their secretions, and **bulk soil**, which constitutes everything else. The microbial profile of the rhizosphere has stark differences to bulk soil. Root systems create microenvironments that favor the growth of specific bacteria. These microenvironments affect the way nutrients and energy are delivered, how water drains, and how temperature fluctuates. Different plants and microbes have specific chemical and metabolic signatures, which in turn change the chemical properties of soil. This interplay between living and nonliving entities defines the characteristics of their respective environments.

<u>The physical structure of soil is determined by the proportions of three main particle types: sand, silt, and clay</u>. These particles clump together to form aggregates of different sizes and textures. Soil with large, coarse particles (sand) or clumps is more permeable than finer soil, allowing the passage of water and faster leaching of soluble molecules. This can deplete the soil of necessary nutrients and limit the amount of life that can be sustained by it. Conversely, soils containing more fine particles (silt and clay)

or smaller clumps are less aerated than coarse soils, restricting the growth of microbes that need oxygen gas (O_2) below the surface.

The rates at which materials are deposited into the soil and subsequently removed or processed by natural forces, such as living organisms and water, drastically impacts the spatial composition of soil. As we dig into the soil, getting further away from the surface, we encounter differences in physical and chemical composition, as well as differences in the microbial populations found at each depth. Cross-sections of most soils reveal that they are divided into distinct layers called **horizons** (Figure 2-1). Understanding the different horizons is important to categorizing soils. The structure of horizons is also a good predictor of the nutritional characteristics of the microbes living within them. Generally, as we descend from one horizon to the next, the abundance of organic components, as well as the exposure to light and oxygen, declines.

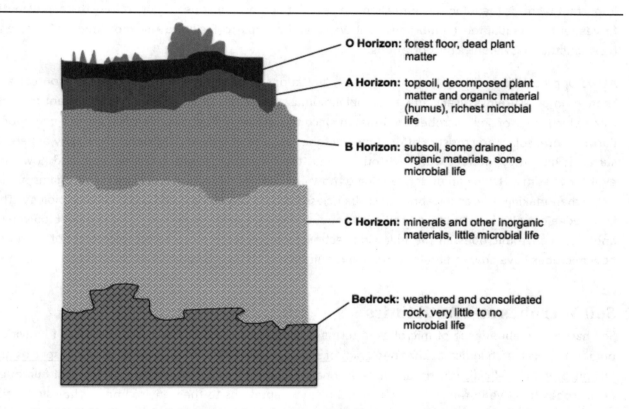

O Horizon: forest floor, dead plant matter

A Horizon: topsoil, decomposed plant matter and organic material (humus), richest microbial life

B Horizon: subsoil, some drained organic materials, some microbial life

C Horizon: minerals and other inorganic materials, little microbial life

Bedrock: weathered and consolidated rock, very little to no microbial life

Figure 2-1. Soil Horizons: Soil is divided into layers called horizons, which vary in their physical and chemical characteristics. As we descend from one horizon to the other, organic matter and microbial life decrease and we approach greater accumulations of inorganic materials, such as minerals and rock.

The **O Horizon** sits at the surface of the soil profile, where un-decomposed plant matter is directly exposed to the elements. This is what we typically see on the forest floor. Right below this thin layer sits the **A Horizon**, or **topsoil**, which is rich in organic matter and contains most soil life. Microbes actively decompose organic material to form humus and intimately interact with plant roots and other organisms, such as fungi, insects, and worms. Some of the organic and inorganic components of this layer are easily drained by water and accumulate in the subsequent **B Horizon**, or subsoil. The B Horizon contains lower levels of microbial life and a greater proportion of anaerobic bacteria that do not require oxygen for respiration. Inorganic matter, such as minerals and partially weathered parent material, constitute the **C Horizon**. In this layer, microbial life is low in abundance but nevertheless present. Researchers have even found microbes in the bedrock, thriving in an environment free from sunlight, oxygen, and organic molecules and with very little available water.

pH is a significant factor in shaping microbial life in soil. Plants and microbes can only survive within a specific pH range. This means that pH can be viewed as reflective of soil health. After comparing different environments across the globe, Fierer and Jackson found that soil pH was the best predictor of microbial diversity. Arid soils, which are poor in water and nutrients but generally have a near-neutral pH, were richer in microbial diversity than rainforest soils, which are usually more acidic (2006). This is in spite of the fact that rainforests comprise incredible amounts of diversity at the **macroscale**. Another important factor is the ionic concentration of the soil. Microbes must be equipped to withstand **osmotic forces** with well-adapted membranes, cell walls, and pumps to facilitate the movement of ions and resist fluctuations in ionic concentrations.

As we approach the bottom layers of the soil, limitations in oxygen, sunlight, and carbon sources and changes in pressure drastically affect microbial biomass, diversity, and nutrition. It is important to know from which layer of soil microbes are isolated since this greatly influences microbial growth conditions. Furthermore, soil characteristics affect how microbes acquire energy and nutrients, how they adhere to surfaces, how they interact with each other, what their life and growth cycles are like, and how they evolve over time. Having an understanding of how environmental factors influence microorganisms can help when making inferences about microbial classification, physiology, and basic cellular biology. This knowledge can also help us make predictions about where we might expect to find the most biodiversity and most active microbes. In the following sections, we will learn more about microbial nutrition and how microbes have adapted their nutritional requirements to their respective environments.

Soil Microbes and Antibiotics

Soil harbors an abundance of microbes in terms of biodiversity and biomass (the number of individual organisms). Research indicates that <u>one gram of soil contains tens of thousands of bacterial species and billions of individual cells</u> (Curtis, Sloan, & Scannell, 2002; Schloss & Handelsman, 2006). **Soil microbes**, or microbes that live in the soil, have evolved many adaptations to their environment. They synthesize an arsenal of biochemicals used for bacterial warfare, signaling, or acquiring nutrients. They break down complex molecules, such as those present in decaying plant matter or carcasses, and cycle nutrients and elements back into their ecosystems. In addition, many soil processes that decompose biological materials release greenhouse gases and characteristic odors. It is no wonder that humans have ascribed so many mystical qualities to soil.

Soil bacteria live in a crowded and highly competitive environment where conditions constantly change and resources are limited. In order to cope with a changing and competitive environment, many microbes have evolved specialized molecules that mediate their interactions with their surroundings. Pigments, toxins, and antibiotics are specialized molecules known as secondary metabolites. **Secondary**

metabolites are organic compounds produced by bacteria that enhance their chances for survival, while remaining nonessential for fundamental growth processes (unlike structural molecules and DNA, for example). Antibiotics are secondary metabolites that inhibit the growth of other microorganisms. In their natural habitat, some microbes may produce antibiotics to reduce competition for resources; these same antibiotics save human lives when used as drugs to treat infectious disease (more on secondary metabolites and antibiotics in Section 9).

The majority of antibiotics in commercial and clinical use today are derived from soil bacteria. Actinomycetes, which are common soil bacteria, produce 60% of clinically important antibiotics. There is still tremendous potential for finding new antibiotics among the immense soil reservoir of microbes and molecules; in fact, the more scientists study soil, the more we realize just how little we know about the chemistry of soil microbes. The vast unknown features and intricacy of the soil makes this ecosystem a fascinating place to study microbes, which is the focus of our research project. We will collect soil and bring it to the lab to explore the capabilities of the microbes living in it. Keep in mind that <u>a soil sample you collect represents the most complex ecosystem on Earth. Your soil sample may not encapsulate the full range of biology and chemistry of soil, or even of the soil immediately adjacent to the sample you removed, but it will be very, very complex. So pay close attention to the characteristics of the soil ecosystem and what they might indicate about the microbes inhabiting it.</u>

- *How will we know whether our sampling location is rich in abundance and diversity of antibiotic-producing bacteria?*

As a collaborative network of student researchers and instructors across the globe – from Malaysia to the United States – the Small World Initiative is poised to collect data at a scale never before reported. By documenting detailed information about your sample location and keeping records of your observations (e.g., the number of microbes isolated and the number of those that produce antibiotics), we will begin to amass a large and useful data set that may reveal trends in soil. This information may prove helpful, not only for future Small World Initiative classes, but also for the research community as a whole, to develop the tools to predict which soils are most likely to be sources of new antibiotics. **Do not forget to include your important data in the Small World Initiative Soil Sample Database: www.smallworldinitiative.org/data**.

Experiment 2: Find a local* soil environment you wish to sample

*Note: Due to federal regulations, soil should only be sampled in the same state as your institution unless you acquire the proper permits and approval.

Biological Questions:
- What soil environments will give us the most unique and greatest diversity of bacteria to study in the lab? Define what unique and diverse means to you.
- What local soil environment will you choose to collect a soil sample and why?
- What do you hypothesize about the abundance and diversity of microbes in your soil sample and why? How will you test this? Think of controls to use in your experiment.

Background:

Objective:

Criteria for picking soil sample:

Soil sample site:

Hypothesis and rationale:

Technique used for collecting your soil sample:

Notes:

Soil Sample Data Collection Sheet – Location & Site Conditions

Adapted from: Kristen Butela – Seton Hill University

Worksheet also available in Research Protocols. **Include your data in the Small World Initiative Soil Sample Database: www.smallworldinitiative.org/data**

*Collected By:	
*General Location:	
GPS Coordinates via Google Earth (e.g., Latitude, Longitude):	
*Date & Time Collected:	
*Sample Site Descriptors:	
Air Temperature (°C):	
Humidity (%):	
Depth (In.):	
Type of Soil:	
Soil Temperature (°C):	
pH of Soil:	
Soil Water Content (%):	
Additional Data to be Determined in Lab (Weather Conditions, Organic Content):	

* Indicates field is required in the Small World Initiative Soil Sample Database.

Additional Documentation:

- Photo of sampling site
- Identification of any plant species observed near site
- Photo of soil in collection tube

Soil Sampling Kit Contents:

- Data sheets
- 50-mL conical tubes
- Lab marker
- "Scientific Soil Sample Collection Device" (plastic knife or spoon)
- Alcohol pads (used to disinfect collection device, thermometer, ruler before taking each sample)
- Thermometer
- Site marking flag (if return to site necessary)
- Plastic ruler

Printout of "Guide of Texture by Feel":
https://www.nrcs.usda.gov/wps/portal/nrcs/detail/soils/edu/kthru6/?cid=nrcs142p2_054311.

Section 3:
Redefining "Growth" and "Culture"

Bacterial Growth

Bacterial cells "grow" to a limited extent (generally doubling in size before dividing), but this is not what microbiologists usually refer to when using the term "growth." We use the word **"growth"** to describe an increase in the size of a microbial population. In other words, when talking about single-celled organisms, "growth" usually means "reproduction." Reproduction is critical to the survival of a species, and bacteria are true survivors, reproducing exponentially under optimal growth conditions.

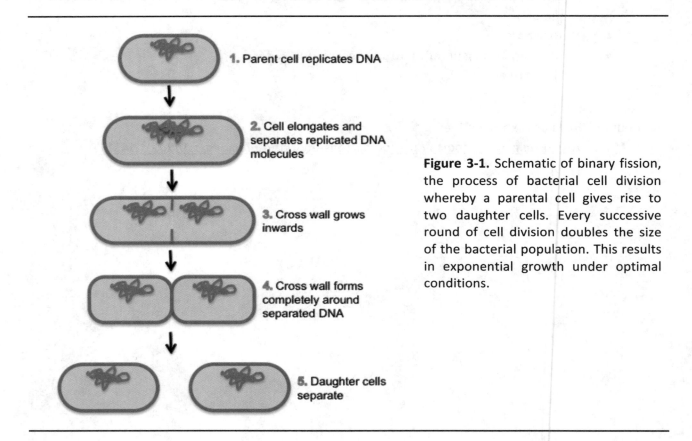

1. Parent cell replicates DNA

2. Cell elongates and separates replicated DNA molecules

3. Cross wall grows inwards

4. Cross wall forms completely around separated DNA

5. Daughter cells separate

Figure 3-1. Schematic of binary fission, the process of bacterial cell division whereby a parental cell gives rise to two daughter cells. Every successive round of cell division doubles the size of the bacterial population. This results in exponential growth under optimal conditions.

The bacterial growth cycle is driven by complex intracellular and extracellular signals, which tell the cell when it is time to replicate. We will not go into those signals because they are beyond the scope of our research. However, we will illustrate the basics of cell division: The first step in the process is DNA synthesis, in which a bacterium makes an extra copy of its chromosome, which contains all the necessary genetic information for the cell to live. The cell then increases in size and elongates, pulling two identical chromosomes apart. Once the chromosomes are localized at the opposite ends of the elongated cell, the plasma membrane and cell wall start forming an "equatorial septum," which splits the parental cell into two daughter cells. This type of symmetrical cell division is known as **binary fission** (Figure 3-1). A few bacteria reproduce by an alternate mechanism known as **budding**, in which a small daughter cell "buds off" a larger mother cell. In either case, daughter cells remain genetically identical to the parent.

In any given population of bacteria, some cells will be dividing, others may be between stages or quiescent, and others may be dying. Yet when conditions are optimal for growth, such as a warm environment with all the right nutrients, most cells will be dividing rapidly, and their population will grow exponentially. The time it takes for a population of bacteria to double in size is called the **doubling, or generation, time**. In rich nutrient environments, *Escherichia coli* populations may double every 20 minutes, whereas other species of bacteria, such as *Mycobacterium tuberculosis*, may take up to 16 hours. "Optimal growth" conditions, however, are virtually nonexistent in natural habitats, where bacteria are kept in check by competing microbes and limited resources. Optimal growth conditions are typically accomplished in the lab, where microbiologists have developed nutrient-rich environments to support the growth of some bacteria.

Bacterial Cultivation

To promote the growth of bacteria in the lab, which is referred to as **culturing** or **cultivating**, we need a medium to provide them nutrition and a place to live and reproduce. **Media** (plural of the word medium) are "bacteriological foods," which are mixtures of nutrients contained in liquid or solid form (more on media and nutrition in Section 4). When a microorganism is introduced into a liquid medium or on the surface of a solid medium and allowed to reproduce, we refer to them as **cultures**. Liquid media are typically referred to as broths, and solid media are called agar plates (Figure 3-2). (Agar is the solidifying agent that is used to make the media solid.) Cultures conditions are carefully controlled for parameters, such as temperature, humidity, and oxygen levels. However, there is no *one* food for bacteria. Just as bacteria are taxonomically diverse, so are their nutritional requirements. Every discovery of a new organism requires a careful assessment of the nutrients and conditions necessary to support its growth, and many cannot be cultured in the lab under standard conditions.

The greatest limiting factor that still persists today is the small number of bacteria that successfully grow in culture. Until the 1990s, most of our knowledge of bacteria was based on the small number of so-called **culturable** bacteria, or bacteria that can be cultured in the lab based on current knowledge. This **culture-dependent** approach has been the basis for studying bacteria in most traditional microbiology labs. However, microbiologists have developed alternative approaches to get a wider and more accurate representation of bacteria living in the environment. This **culture-independent** approach does not require bacteria to reproduce in the lab or exist in large numbers. However, it relies on advanced and expensive equipment to detect and analyze millions of microscopic entities individually. **Metagenomics**, the study of all the genetic material present in a given environment, allows us to sample soil and analyze all the DNA present in it as a signature for all the organisms living in it, whether or not they grow in the lab. These methods indicate that <u>only 0.3% of all bacteria in soil can be cultured in the lab</u> (Amann, Ludwig, & Schleifer, 1995). This means that only 3 in 1,000 bacteria can be studied in the laboratory by using a culture-dependent approach.

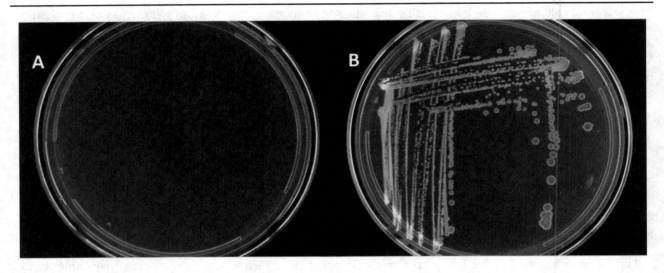

Figure 3-2. (A) A solid medium, composed of a mix of nutrients, water, and agar (a solidifying agent) with no bacterial growth. (B) The same solid medium with culture of *Staphylococcus cohnii* after 48 hours of incubation at 28°C.

The limitations of the culture-dependent approach result from inadequate knowledge of conditions that favor bacterial growth in natural habitats. Studying the soil metagenome in many ways has led to more questions than answers. Although the metagenome represents the complexity of the microbial world, its functional diversity remains difficult to study without culturing bacteria. In our lab, we will rely on the culture-dependent approach to study soil bacteria because it gives us functional information, can lead directly to antibiotic discovery, and has not been used to fully mine the soil or the antibiotic-producing bacteria that inhabit it.

CFUs and Bacterial Colonies

The most important feature of the culture-dependent approach is that it allows us to study microscopic entities at the macroscopic scale. However, it is important to keep in mind the requirements and limitations of this approach:

1. *Only **viable** (alive and capable of reproducing) cells will grow. Dead and/or dormant cells will not be detected.*
2. *Only cells that are **culturable** (capable of growth on the selected culture medium and under the prescribed incubation conditions) will be detected. Cells that cannot grow under the selected laboratory conditions will not be detected.*

In order to detect a microorganism in the lab, we need a visual cue that will tell us whether or not the microorganism meets the above requirements. We are all familiar with the appearance of molds on bread and other food, and we use the visual cue to avoid eating contaminated food. Similarly, when we grow bacteria in the lab, we typically look for the formation of colonies. In the field of microbiology, a **colony** is a collection of genetically identical cells that arise from a single cell. This can be any one cell in the environment or in a soil sample. Single cells that give rise to a colony are referred to as **CFUs (colony**

forming units). As a CFU reproduces, the mass of dividing cells eventually becomes large enough that a macroscopic colony becomes visible to the naked eye. Colonies enable us to see into the microscopic world, each colony revealing characteristics that are unique to its species and which, in many cases, can be easily recognizable by experienced microbiologists (more on colony morphology in Section 5).

An important step in isolating soil bacteria is obtaining **single colonies**. We know that, by definition, a colony arises from a single CFU. Therefore, we can expect all the cells present in the colony to be of the same genetic composition. By studying bacterial species discretely, we can truly appreciate the diversity of microbes and their unique characteristics. However, how do we go from millions of individual cells and species living in soil to single colonies on a solid medium? Even if only 3 in 1,000 bacteria in the soil will grow in the lab, there will still be tens and hundreds of thousands of colonies growing on the surface of a solid medium (e.g., a Petri dish) all crammed together. The outcome of this will be a nondescript mass of contiguous and overlapping colonies that provides no useful information about the types of microorganisms in the sample. The logical solution would be to spread them out, but how much room do we need to spread out thousands of CFUs so they would grow into non-overlapping, distinct colonies?

Microbiologists use dilution methods to reduce the number of cells present in a given sample. We may dilute them in pure water or in salty solutions to keep the cells in an isotonic environment. Once we obtain a desired dilution, which can only be determined on a case-by-case basis, we can spread a small volume of the dilution (in the range of microliters) on a plate. The spreading step separates and disperses cells all over the surface of the plate. Each CFU will be randomly deposited on a spot on the plate, where it will proliferate and give rise to a single colony. Colonies will be sparse and separated when the appropriate dilution is achieved (Figure 3-3).

Since colonies represent the unique qualities of the bacteria reproducing in them, we must ensure that they are not contaminated with other species that may obscure our observations (Figure 3-3C). To confirm that a colony contains a single species of bacteria, microbiologists use other spreading methods to further separate cells and observe differences in morphology (more on colony morphology in Section 5). Obtaining **pure cultures**, which each contain a single strain of bacteria, is important for conducting controlled experiments and is the basis of making comparisons, reliable observations, and measures in scientific research. By observing the response of a pure culture to different variables (e.g., type of medium used, temperature, incubation period, technique used, chemicals applied), we can make inferences about the characteristics of individual cells that constitute it.

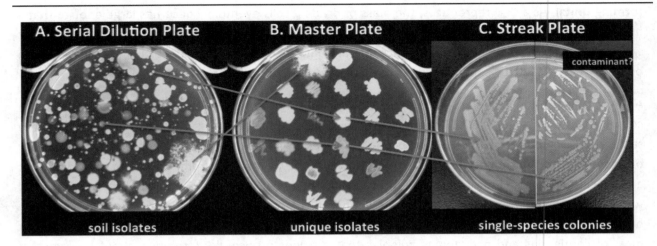

Figure 3-3. (A) A serial dilution plate of a rich soil sample. Bacteria in the soil sample were suspended in sterile water and diluted 10,000-fold (10^{-4}) to obtain a distribution of cells that produces discrete colonies, while representing a wide diversity of bacteria. After incubating the plate 24–72 hours, single colonies can then be picked from the dilution plate and smeared on a new medium plate to create a master plate. (B) The master plate serves as a catalogue of the visibly distinct bacteria that were isolated from a sample. The blue arrows show the transfer of cells from colonies in the dilution plate to a clear spot on the master plate. After 24–72 hours of incubation, the smear grows onto a dense patch of cells that is visible to the naked eye. From this collection of cells, we start new cultures and do further testing. (C) The unique isolates on the master plate are "streaked" onto a new plate to isolate single colonies. A streak of one of the isolates (far right) reveals a second species of bacteria interspersed in the patch. The streaking method allows us to separate them and start a pure culture.

References

Amann, R. I., Ludwig, W., & Schleifer, K. H. (1995). Phylogenetic identification and in situ detection of individual microbial cells without cultivation. Microbiol Rev, 59:143-169.

Curtis, T. P., Sloan, W. T., & Scannell, J. W. (2002). Estimating prokaryotic diversity and its limits. Proc Natl Acad Sci U S A, 99:10494-10499. doi: 10.1073/pnas.14268019.

Schloss, P. D., & Handelsman, J. (2006). Toward a census of bacteria in soil. PLoS Comput Biol, 2:e92. doi: 10.1371/journal.pcbi.0020092.

Milestones in Microbiology

Selman Waksman coined the term "antibiotic" and pioneered exploration of the prolific antibiotic producers of the soil during the 1940s and 1950s. Along with his student Albert Schatz, he discovered and developed the antibiotic streptomycin, produced by the actinomycete *Streptomyces griseus*. Streptomycin was the cure for tuberculosis. Wakman's discovery, along with the commercialization of penicillin, ushered in the golden age of antibiotics, a time in which the rate of antibiotic discovery was rampant, with dozens of antibiotics being discovered and brought to the market every year. By the beginning of the 1980s, it was believed that antibiotics had eliminated the threat of infectious disease.

Photo source: commons.wikimedia.org (public domain).

Alma Whiffen, a contemporary of Waksman, was a mycologist who discovered the antifungal agent cycloheximide during the mid-1940s, produced by *S. griseus* (the same bacterium that produced the antibiotic streptomycin). Because of its toxicity to eukaryotic cells (such as human cells), cycloheximide is normally used for research applications, such as inhibiting the growth of fungi in bacterial cultures.

Photo source: commons.wikimedia.org (public domain).

Experiment 3: Find a method to isolate single colonies of bacteria from your soil sample

Biological Questions:
- What is the significance of single colonies? How can you obtain single colonies on a medium plate from a soil sample?
- How will you enumerate the culturable microorganisms present in your soil sample?
- Once you obtain single colonies, can you identify morphologically distinct microorganisms?
- What would you like to learn about the microorganisms you isolated?

Background:

Objective:

Hypothesis and rationale:

Procedure for obtaining single colonies on plate:

Draw a schematic of the procedure used:

Data and observations:

Interpretations and conclusions:

Notes:

Assignment: Calculating CFU/g soil

Objective:

Sample:	Number of colonies per sample				
Media	No dilution	10^{-1}	10^{-2}	10^{-3}	10^{-4}

CFU/g soil calculations:

How does this compare with the literature?

Notes:

*Don't forget to upload your data: www.smallworldinitiative.org/data

Laboratory Data Collection Summary Sheet

While you conduct your research, you may wish to track the following information to compare with other researchers. **Upload your findings online:** *www.smallworldinitiative.org/data*

General Metrics: Isolates

# of bacterial isolates picked	
# of isolates tested for antibiotic activity	
# of isolates positive for antibiotic activity	

Spectrum of Activity

# of isolates with activity against each strain/# of isolates tested against each strain:								
Gram-positive				Gram-negative				
Enterococcus raffinosus	*Bacillus subtilis*	*Staphylococcus epidermidis*	*Mycobacterium smegmatis*	*Acinetobacter baylyi*	*Escherichia coli*	*Erwinia carotovora*	*Enterobacter aerogenes*	*Pseudomonas putida*
/	/	/	/	/	/	/	/	/

# of isolates with positive activity against "n" tester strains								
1	2	3	4	5	6	7	8	9

Activity Against Gram-Negative & Gram-Positive Bacteria

# of isolates positive for only Gram-positive activity	
# of isolates positive for only Gram-negative activity	
# of isolates positive for both Gram-positive and Gram-negative	

Sequencing

# of isolates sent for 16S rRNA sequencing	
# of isolates with definitive sequencing results	

Extracts

# of isolates on which extraction attempted	
# of extracts produced in sufficient quantity for antibiotic testing	
# of extracts tested for antibiotic activity	
# of extracts confirmed to have antibiotic activity	

Chemical Structure

# of chemical structures determined	
# of novel chemical structures	

Additional Assay Summaries from Your Class (below are two examples):

# of isolates/extracts with hemolytic activity	
# of isolates/extracts with eukaryotic activity (specify anti-fungal, lethal to C. elegans, etc.)	

Section 4:
Bacteria Are What They Eat, Too

Composition of Living Things

We have considered methods to maximize the number of bacteria in a sample. But did those efforts also capture the number of different species? Will all species present in the soil grow equally well on a given media type? To answer these questions, we must consider how microorganisms obtain the energy needed to support biological processes and proliferation.

Like all other organisms, microorganisms use energy to produce organic molecules that perform specific biological functions and allow them to grow, proliferate, and engage with their environments. Organic molecules by definition contain carbon (C) atoms, the core elemental building block of life, and are the main constituents of cellular components and energy sources. Some organic molecules can be joined together to form complex macromolecules (see Table 4-1), which perform their own specific functions, or be further modified by reactions within the cell to form secondary metabolites. Organic molecules are largely constructed only from a few elements. Of these elements, carbon (C), hydrogen (H), oxygen (O), nitrogen (N), phosphorus (P), and sulfur (S) are most abundant and required for life. A variety of additional elements are also needed by living cells but in lesser quantities (see Table 4-2).

Organic molecule	Elemental components	Macromolecule
Amino acids	C, H, O, N, S	Proteins
Nucleic acids	C, H, O, N, P	DNA and RNA
Fatty acids	C, H, O	Lipids
Sugars	C, H, O	Carbohydrates

Table 4-1. Macromolecules and their constituents.

Sodium (Na^+)	Magnesium (Mg^{2+})	Calcium (Ca^{2+})
Iron (Fe^{2+}/Fe^{3+})	Potassium (K^+)	Chloride (Cl^-)

Table 4-2. Trace elements. Table adapted from Slonczewski & Foster (2011)

Classifying Bacteria Based on Nutrition

Bacteria can be classified based on how they obtain carbon and energy from their environments to make biological molecules (Table 4-3). Some organisms produce organic molecules by obtaining or "fixing" carbon from inorganic sources, such as CO_2. They are known as **autotrophs** and are the primary producers in food chains. Photosynthetic organisms, such as plants, algae, and cyanobacteria, are good examples of autotrophs. Conversely, **heterotrophs** obtain carbon from organic molecules formed by other organisms. Animals, protozoa, fungi, and many bacteria and archaea are heterotrophs.

Bacteria can also be classified based on their tolerance for oxygen. Many (but not all) bacteria that live in contact with the atmosphere, which is approximately 21% oxygen gas (O_2) by volume, are **aerobic**, which means they can grow and survive in the presence of O_2. In contrast, O_2 is toxic to some anaerobes, many of which thrive only in strictly O_2-free environments.

Living organisms use oxidizing substances, such as O_2, sulfate (SO_4^{2-}), and pyruvate, as electron acceptors in fueling reactions that oxidize "food" molecules to free usable energy. These processes of respiration (using oxygen as a source of electrons) and fermentation (using organic molecules as a source of electrons) ultimately capture and store released energy in the form of **adenosine triphosphate** (**ATP**), the "energy currency" common to all life.

		Energy Source	
		Light (photo-)	**Chemical Compounds (chemo-)**
Carbon Source	**Carbon dioxide (auto-)**	**Photoautotrophs** • Plants, algae, cyanobacteria • Green sulfur and purple sulfur bacteria	**Chemoautotrophs** • Hydrogen, sulfur, nitrifying bacteria
	Organic (hetero-)	**Photoheterotrophs** • Green nonsulfur and purple nonsulfur bacteria	**Chemoheterotrophs** • Aerobic respiration: most animals, fungi, and protozoa; many bacteria

Table 4-3: Metabolic types of organisms are categorized on the basis of how they obtain their energy and carbon. Table adapted from Bauman, Microbiology 1st ed., Figure 6.1.

Media and Culture Conditions

In the lab, microbes are grown on many different types of media that contain mixes of essential nutrients suspended in water (e.g., broths and infusions). Some media are solidified with agar, gelatin, or another jelly-like substance. Media ingredients range from dehydrated extracts of plant, animal, or fungal material to synthetic compounds made in the lab. Media can be enriched with a variety of organic molecules, macromolecules, and vitamins to support the growth of **fastidious** bacteria, which have complex nutritional requirements. They can also be minimal, composed mainly of simple sugars, salts, and water. Over the years, microbiologists have developed standard media formulations that can be purchased from commercial vendors and used for many different applications.

Other **physical parameters**, such as light exposure, temperature, and tonicity, can drastically affect the composition of microbes that grow in culture. The composition and concentration of ions and molecules in a bacterium's environment not only influence its nutrition, but also the overall stability of its cells. A medium with inadequate **electrolytes** may represent a hypotonic environment that will cause cells to swell up and burst. Conversely, a hypertonic medium with an excessively high concentration of solutes may cause cells to lose water, shrivel, and die. Similarly, many bacteria cannot survive outside a relatively narrow pH range.

Growth on a plate indicates that the bacteria are living within an acceptable range of conditions that allows them to survive and proliferate. It does not mean that all of their needs are met. Like all living things, bacteria are hard-wired to respond to stimuli in their environments. Cellular processes, such as gene expression, are mediated by factors and complex pathways that scientists do not fully understand and cannot account for in the laboratory. For example, many scientists are trying to stimulate the expression of **silent genes** encoding production of potentially novel secondary metabolites in various species of the genus *Streptomyces*.

Finding the right combination of conditions and stimuli that promote the growth of certain bacteria or induce the expression of certain genes is perhaps the biggest obstacle to unraveling the biodiversity and biosynthetic potential of microbes. Increasingly, research shows that many bacteria are dependent on microbial communities where they exchange signals, genetic material, nutrients, and other stimuli that trigger specific responses in cells. There are more variables than any experiment can test, but the more ways we isolate and grow bacteria, the more we can learn about the organisms in a sample. Use your imagination.

References

Mukhopadhyaya, P. N., Deb, C., Lahiri, C., & Roy, P. (2000). A soxA gene, encoding a diheme cytochrome C, and a sox locus, essential for sulfur oxidation in a new sulfur lithotrophic bacterium. J Bacteriol, 182:4278-4287.

Slonczewski, J., & Foster, J. W. (2011). *Microbiology: An Evolving Science* (2nd ed.). New York: W.W. Norton & Co.

10 μm

Living on a Bacterial Planet

The long chains (filaments) of the sulfur-oxidizing bacterium *Beggiatoa*, seen under the microscope under high magnification (notice the scale in the picture). This microorganism is an example of a lithotroph, which derives its nutrition from inorganic molecules, such as reduced inorganic compounds and minerals typically found in rocks, hence the name, "rock eaters." Lithotrophs, composed of both bacteria and archaea, live in extreme environments ranging from bedrock to deep hydrothermal vents. The sulfur-oxidizing bacterium *Beggiatoa* was the first example of a lithotrophic bacterium discovered in microbial mats near hydrothermal vents and sulfur-rich environments in the ocean bottom. *Beggiatoa* oxidizes sulfur compounds such as sulfide (S^{2-}) as their energy source and carbon dioxide (CO_2) as a carbon source (Mukhopadhyaya, Deb, Lahiri, & Roy, 2000)

Photo source: <http://www.mbl.edu/services/research/cmf/> Date accessed: 21 November 2016.

Experiment 4: Choose your own media and culture conditions

Biological Questions:
- How can we optimize media and culture conditions to favor the growth of diverse microorganisms in your soil sample?
- What medium and culture conditions do you choose and why?
- How do your conditions of choice compare with your isolates' natural habitat?

Background:

Objective:

Medium of choice and rationale:

Culture condition choices:

    Temperature:

    Oxygen level:

    Other:

Hypothesis and rationale:

Experimental design and techniques used:

Control and treatments:

Data and observations:

Interpretations and conclusions:

Notes:

Soil Sample Data Collection Sheet – Culture Conditions & Medium Data

Don't forget to update your entry and include your data in the Small World Initiative Soil Sample Database: www.smallworldinitiative.org/data

Type of Medium:	
Growth Temperature (°C):	
Oxygen Environment (e.g., aerobic, partially anaerobic, atmospheric oxygen):	
Length of Incubation (hours):	
CFU/g:	
Total Number of Morphologically Diverse Colonies Isolated (i.e., # of patches on master plate):	
Notes/Additional Culture Conditions	

*Repeat the above for additional culture conditions and media data.

Section 5: Solid Versus Liquid Cultures

Colony Morphology

Since bacteria were first cultured on solid media, microbiologists have noticed that colonies differ in color, texture, shape, and margin or edges. Works like *Bergey's Manual of Systematic Bacteriology* contain exhaustive descriptions of the physical and biochemical attributes of bacteria and have helped microbiologists identify and classify bacteria for nearly a century. **Colony morphology** is one of the first characteristics used to distinguish a particular organism from unrelated species of bacteria and other groups of microbes. So it is important that we describe the physical characteristics of our microbes when isolated from the environment (Figure 5-1).

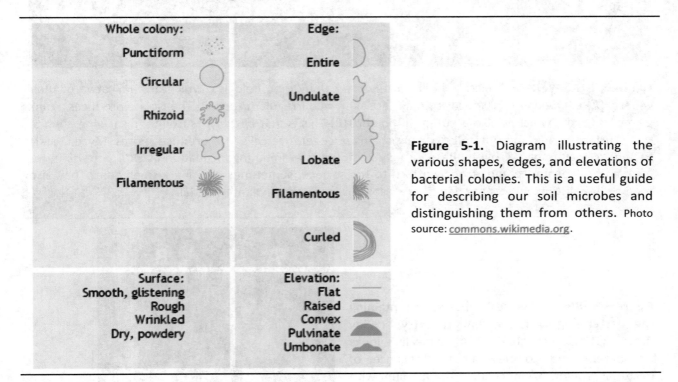

Figure 5-1. Diagram illustrating the various shapes, edges, and elevations of bacterial colonies. This is a useful guide for describing our soil microbes and distinguishing them from others. Photo source: commons.wikimedia.org.

Bacteria express characteristic colony morphologies. For example, *Lysobacter* and *Pseudomonas* colonies are typically slimy and irregular in shape and may fluoresce under UV light (Figure 5-2A). *Streptomyces* colonies have bold colors and develop a white fuzzy surface, which contains spores (Figure 5-2B). *Bacillus* colonies may sprawl thinly over the agar and typically show relatively dull, bland colors.

Unfortunately, in the prokaryotic world, morphology does not reliably indicate relatedness and is therefore inadequate to identify an unknown organism. Ultimately, morphology only provides us with a hint, and morphological observation is only the first step of many when attempting to identify a bacterial isolate. To assign a family, genus, or species, we need much more additional information acquired through further testing. In future sections, we will explore more reliable and modern approaches to bacterial identification.

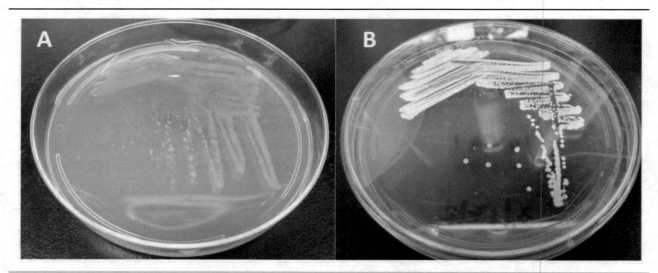

Figure 5-2 [Above]. Two microbes with distinctive colony morphologies, which are indicative of their genera. **(A)** *Lysobacter antibioticus* colonies are slimy and irregular in shape. The isolate produces a pink pigment, myxin, which is also a potent antibiotic. **(B)** This is a *Streptomyces* isolate, displaying a white fuzzy surface, made up of mycelia, or long chains of vegetative cells that produce spores. Mycelia start to appear in stationary growth phase, usually 72 hours after initiating incubation at 28°C. *Streptomyces* have a dry appearance and strongly attach to the surface, sometimes creating a small dent. They also produce the distinctive scent of damp forest soil covered in dead plant material.

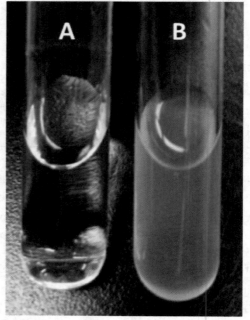

Figure 5-3 [Right]. Two test tubes each containing the bacterial growth medium 10% Tryptic Soy Broth (TSA). **(A)** 10% TSA typically looks transparent and colorless in the absence of bacterial growth. **(B)** Inoculating the medium with a colony of *Lysobacter antibioticus* produces a pink culture after 24–36 hours of growth at 28°C. This microorganism retains its distinctive characteristic – the pigment – in both liquid and solid culture.

Growth Phases

Solid cultures are advantageous because culturable cells proliferate where they were deposited, giving us the opportunity to isolate pure cultures and observe their distinctive morphologies. The opposite is true for liquid media. The fluid nature of liquid cultures allows cells to move randomly throughout the medium. Therefore, to effectively study bacteria in liquid culture, we typically inoculate the medium from a known pure culture, such as a single colony on a solid medium. By doing so, we are assured that the liquid culture remains a pure culture as long as appropriate aseptic technique has been practiced.

Liquid cultures are particularly suitable for studying bacterial growth, or **growth kinetics**, and biochemistry at different growth phases (Slonczewski & Foster, 2011, p. 126). Unlike a solid culture where cells are normally in direct contact with one another and/or their substrate, cells in liquid culture are in a **planktonic,** or free-floating, state. This allows them to move throughout the medium and, if properly shaken during growth, form uniformly mixed cultures. Many bacteria require their liquid environment to be continually aerated and mixed. Therefore, liquid cultures are often grown with the assistance of shaker platforms. Caution must be exercised, however – although good for bacteria that can thrive in a planktonic state, shaking is not advisable for organisms that prefer a solid substrate. Many soil bacteria are not suited for planktonic growth, and therefore, when transferred from solid to liquid culture, there is a decline in the number of viable cells.

Bacterial growth can be approximated by measuring how much light of a particular wavelength (600 nm) is absorbed by a liquid culture over time. This is done with an instrument called a **spectrophotometer**, which measures absorption as **optical density units (ODs).** As cell concentration increases, the liquid culture becomes more cloudy or turbid. As the **turbidity** of the culture increases, the OD value reported by the spectrophotometer will also increase. The mathematical relationship between OD and cell concentration can be used to determine rates of bacterial growth over time. When OD is plotted versus incubation time, we obtain a **standard growth curve** (Figure 5-4), which is a useful model for keeping track of how a population of cells in liquid culture change over time or predicting future behavior of the same isolate. The model shows that bacteria undergo various phases of growth in liquid culture. Growth phases are indicative of what their cells are doing physiologically and metabolically.

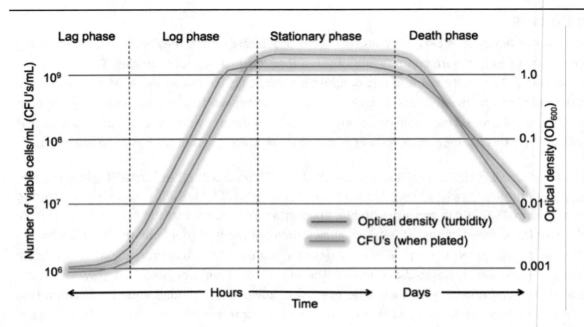

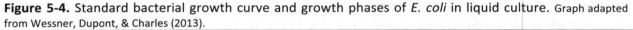

Figure 5-4. Standard bacterial growth curve and growth phases of *E. coli* in liquid culture. Graph adapted from Wessner, Dupont, & Charles (2013).

When cells are first transferred into a new medium, they will enter a period known as the **lag phase** during which very little growth occurs. During this period, the cells are taking cues from the environment and making metabolic adjustments, altering patterns of gene expression to accommodate the new conditions. Once this process has completed, the cells will begin to divide rapidly. Microbiologists typically work with bacteria in the **logarithmic ("log") phase**, where cells are found reproducing exponentially. Bacteria in this phase are highly metabolically active, consuming nutrients in the medium and synthesizing macromolecules to make new cells.

Secondary metabolites, such as pigments and antibiotics, are normally produced toward the end of the log phase as cell concentration peaks and nutrients become depleted. Bacteria in the genus *Streptomyces* have been found to enter into secondary metabolism after they cease to produce essential cellular components, such as DNA (Bibb, 1996). Therefore, for this microorganism, antibiotic production occurs in a growth-phase-dependent manner, which is in turn influenced by nutrient availability in the medium. As nutrients are depleted and waste products accumulate, growth slows such that the number of cells dividing is approximately equal to those dying. This is called **stationary phase**, which can last hours to days depending on the cells' response to a lack of nutrients and an increasingly toxic environment. Eventually, the number of dying cells surpasses the number of living and reproducing cells, and the culture enters the **death phase**.

Spores

Many markers of bacterial growth phases are also visible in solid culture. Over time, colonies stop spreading on the agar and may even begin to shrivel. This occurs as nutrients are depleted, waste and toxic chemicals build up, and water evaporates from the agar matrix. Cells of some bacterial species enter a dormant state and survive for weeks, whereas others have evolved the ability to generate inactive and sometimes highly resistant cells called **spores**. Various types of soil bacteria sporulate after undergoing long vegetative growth and exhausting carbon sources in the medium. *Streptomyces* species undergo various visible transformations, which are indicative of the start of spore production (Figure 5-2B). They form mycelia, which are long chains of vegetative cells that resemble the appearance of fungi. The production of mycelia typically correlates with the onset of secondary metabolism, when these species produce a wide variety of antibiotics (Manteca, Alvarez, Salazar, Yague, & Sanchez, 2008). Soon after, the vegetative mycelia form septa that break up filaments into segments that give rise to reproductive exospores (Figure 5-5A).

Bacillus and *Clostridium* species can produce particularly long-lived and durable **endospores** (Figure 5-5B). As environmental conditions become increasingly unfavorable to support metabolically active cells, the endospores are released and the parent cells die. Spores' remarkable tolerance to extreme dryness, heat, subfreezing temperatures, toxic chemicals, and radiation allows these cells to remain dormant for long periods of time. There have been reliable reports of the successful germination of 100,000-year-old endospores, and even (somewhat controversial) reports of 25-40 million-year-old spore germination (Nicholson et al., 2000). Avoiding contamination with long-lived endospores is the primary reason that lab supplies must be autoclaved in order to achieve sterilization. Autoclaving involves exposure to pressurized steam at 15 PSI and 121°C for a suitable period of time. (15 minutes is appropriate for small volumes.)

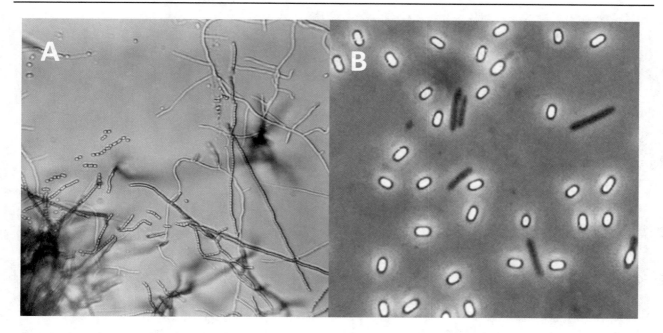

Figure 5-5. Two different types of bacterial spores observed under phase contrast at 400× **[left]** and 1000× **[right]** magnification. **[Left]** *Streptomyces* sp. mycelial filaments and long chains of exospores. **[Right]** *Bacillus* sp. endospores appear as bright, dense structures under the microscope. Photo sources: [Left] commons.wikimedia.org (credit to CDC Public Health Image Library); [Right] commons.wikimedia.org.

References

Bibb, M. (1996). The regulation of antibiotic production in *Streptomyces coelicolor* A3(2). Microbiology, 142:1335-1344.

Manteca, A., Alvarez, R., Salazar, N., Yague, P., & Sanchez, J. (2008). Mycelium differentiation and antibiotic production in submerged cultures of *Streptomyces coelicolor*. Appl Environ Microbiol;74:3877-3886. doi: 10.1128/AEM.02715-07.

Nicholson, W. L., Munakata, N., Horneck, G., Melosh, H. J., & Setlow, P. (2000). Resistance of Bacillus endospores to extreme terrestrial and extraterrestrial environments. Microbiol Mol Biol Rev;64:548-572.

Slonczewski, J., & Foster, J. W. (2011). *Microbiology: An Evolving Science* (2nd ed.). New York: W.W. Norton.

Wessner, D. R., Dupont, C., & Charles, T. (2013). Microbiology. *Print*.

Experiment 5: Isolate unique colonies to test for antibiotic production

Biological Questions:
- What criteria will you use to pick unique colonies from your plates?
- Assuming you cannot test ALL of your bacterial isolates for antibiotic production, how will you prioritize the isolates you choose to study in order to increase the likelihood of obtaining an antibiotic producer?
- What are the qualities of the isolates you have picked for further studying?

Background:

Objective:

Hypothesis and rationale:

Protocol:

Results:

Number of isolates picked:

Characteristics of isolates:

Interpretations and conclusions:

Notes:

Don't forget to update your entry and include your data in the Small World Initiative Soil Sample Database: *www.smallworldinitiative.org/data*

Section 6: Meet the ESKAPE Pathogens

Understanding Infectious Disease

Since ancient times, many diseases, including cholera and the plague, were attributed to miasmas, or "bad air." People believed that pests and parasites associated with plagues, decay, and spoilage could arise from inanimate, or nonliving, matter. This idea – known as **spontaneous generation** – along with the miasma theory greatly hindered preindustrial society from making the connection between microbes and disease and prevented development of effective strategies for prevention and control of disease outbreaks.

In the mid-1800s, **John Snow** helped dispel some of these misconceptions by describing the mode of transmission of cholera. He discovered the source of a particular cholera outbreak in London – a communal water pump in a filthy and densely populated neighborhood. The water source had been contaminated by sewage runoff from a house inhabited by cholera victims. The outbreak killed hundreds of people who drank water from the pump. Snow's detailed epidemiological data led to the disabling of the pump and increased awareness of water quality, public hygiene, and sanitation.

During the same time period, **Louis Pasteur**, a French chemist and microbiologist, helped disprove the theory of spontaneous generation. In an elegant experiment, he showed that sterilized broth, similar to the growth medium we use in the lab, does not spontaneously generate microorganisms from nonliving components. Instead, microbial growth originates as contamination introduced via the surrounding air. This finding was particularly important in an era when food spoilage was common, leading to great losses in disease-ridden industrial cities where food was already scarce. Pasteur realized that the key to preservation was to reduce the number of bacteria present in foods and beverages by applying heat in a process that came to be known as **pasteurization**.

Pasteur's revolutionary work supported the **germ theory of disease**, which states that microorganisms like bacteria are the cause of infectious disease. At the same time, scientists were also becoming aware that microorganisms were virtually everywhere and had useful applications as well. Yeast were shown to be responsible for the fermentation of grape juice to produce wine, and bacterial fermentation was found to convert milk to yogurt.

Work by the German physician **Robert Koch** provided the means to identify **pathogens**, or disease-causing microorganisms. While performing experiments to identify the agents responsible for tuberculosis and anthrax, Koch established a series of criteria, or "postulates," that could be applied to identify pathogens responsible for other infectious diseases as well:

1. *The microbe is always present in diseased individuals but not healthy individuals.*
2. *The microbe is isolated from the infected individual and grown in a pure culture.*
3. *The microbe in the pure culture is introduced into a healthy individual, and the same disease occurs.*

4. *The microbe is reisolated from the sick individual and shown to be the same as the original.*

This process might seem second nature to us today, but in the late 1800s, it was revolutionary. Koch successfully identified *Bacillus anthracis* and *Mycobacterium tuberculosis* as the causative agents of anthrax and tuberculosis, respectively, and was awarded the Nobel Prize in Physiology or Medicine in 1905. Koch's simple and logical criteria continue to help modern clinical microbiologists identify pathogens. Today, the link between microbes and disease is well understood; this knowledge has allowed us to develop effective measures to prevent and treat infectious disease around the world. Nevertheless, humanity remains at risk from diseases caused by microorganisms.

Pathogens that were once believed to have been conquered during the golden age of antibiotics (see Section 7) are now reemerging in drug-resistant forms, and they are doing so at an accelerating rate. As a result, we are effectively running out of treatment options. Hospitals have become havens for multidrug-resistant "superbugs," and the widespread misuse of antibiotics in households and in agricultural practices around the world means that drug-resistant pathogens are emerging as a threat in our homes. The process by which pathogens acquire resistance is only partially understood and is an important area of ongoing research (see Section 10), but the trends we see today point to a grim future if we do not find effective solutions based on drug deployment, hygiene, or other practices.

Choosing Test Organisms

- *Since antibiotics do not affect all bacteria equally, how will you decide which organism to test your microbe against?*

As we isolate individual microbes, we hope that some will produce antibiotics at detectable levels. Initially, for practical reasons, researchers assay these microbes for the ability to inhibit the growth of only a single or small number of test organisms. Microbes that show activity may later be screened against a broader panel of test organisms.

- *Does the antibiotic's ability to inhibit the growth of one test organism indicate that the antibiotic will inhibit all bacteria?*

Because prokaryotes differ in their anatomical and physiological traits, different organisms may be more or less susceptible to the effects of any particular antibiotic. Some antibiotics are **broad spectrum**, meaning that they affect a wide range of bacteria. Others antibiotics have a **narrow spectrum** of activity. One anatomical feature that plays a significant role in the susceptibility of a microbe to a particular antibiotic is its cell wall composition (discussed in Section 8).

- *How can we detect the production of antibiotics? How do we distinguish the producers from the nonproducers?*

In Section 7, we will conduct experiments to screen our isolates for their ability to produce antibiotics. But first, we must decide which microbe to test our isolates against.

The ESKAPE Pathogens

When choosing a test organism, a logical choice is an organism that is clinically relevant – i.e., a human pathogen. Today, there are six organisms that are considered to be major threats, not because they cause the most devastating illnesses but because they comprise the majority of antibiotic-resistant infections seen in healthcare settings. They are *Enterococcus faecium, Staphylococcus aureus, Klebsiella pneumoniae, Acinetobacter baumannii, Pseudomonas aeruginosa,* and several species of *Enterobacter* (**ESKAPE**).

The leading author of a 2009 report on Clinical Infectious Diseases, Helen Boucher, MD, stated:

> These [ESKAPE pathogens] are among the biggest threats infectious disease physicians face today…We desperately need new drugs to fight them. But we also need cooperation among industry, academia, and government to create a sustainable R&D [research and development] infrastructure that will fill the pipeline to meet today's needs and keep it filled with drugs that tackle tomorrow's infectious diseases threats.

ESKAPE Pathogen	Safe Relative
Enterococcus faecium	*Enterococcus raffinosus*
Staphylococcus aureus	*Staphylococcus epidermidis*
Klebsiella pneumoniae	*Escherichia coli*
Acinetobacter baumannii	*Acinetobacter baylyi*
Pseudomonas aeruginosa	*Pseudomonas putida*
Enterobacter species	*Enterobacter aerogenes*

Table 6-1. The ESKAPE pathogens and their safe relatives. The Small World Initiative uses these safe ESKAPE relatives.

Although it would be ideal to test the ability of our isolates to inhibit the growth of all or at least a subset of these organisms, it is not possible to do so in a teaching laboratory due to their potential to cause human disease. However, we can take advantage of evolution and test our isolates against closely related organisms that do not pose a health risk. These "safe relatives" have many of the same anatomical and physiological features of their respective ESKAPE counterparts. Yet they are safe enough to be studied in teaching laboratories following basic biosafety protocols.

Not All Bacteria Are Harmful

Although pathogenic bacteria get most of the attention (for good reason), you should realize that humans are constantly associated with bacteria in our bodies, in the foods we eat, and in the environment. If you were to examine every cell in and on your body, you would find that the majority of them are not actually human! The members of the **human microbiome**, the microbes that reside in and on our bodies, outnumber our own cells at least three to one. Research has shown that our cells are "constantly bathed" in bacterial metabolites (Slonczewski & Foster, 2011). Therefore, there can be no doubt that microbes intimately and substantially influence our lives and our health.

The human gut, which houses 100 billion bacteria per cm^3, thrives with bacterial activity that is responsible for 15-20% of our caloric intake (Slonczewski & Foster, 2011, p. 868). This **consortium** of microorganisms is composed of organisms, including members of the *Bacteroides, Clostridium,* and *Escherichia* genera, among many others. Disruption of the gut microbiota can cause many different metabolic and physiological disorders.

Various Gram-positive bacteria, including *Staphylococcus* and *Bacillus*, colonize our skin and are also part of the normal human microbiome. They are not simply passive bystanders but are an important part of our first line of defense against infection and act as active inducers of proper immune function. In an experiment by Belkaid et al., mice with *Staphylococcus epidermidis* on their skin were found to have a better immune response than germ-free mice (Naik et al., 2012).

Probiotics, microbes that are consumed to improve health, are found in many fermented products, including yogurt. Pharmacologist John Cryan carried out experiments to test the neurological effects of administering doses of probiotics to mice. He found that certain probiotics had impressive effects on mouse stress and anxiety levels. Mice treated with probiotics were more willing to walk out into the open and take action to protect themselves from a perceived threat of drowning, behaviors suggestive of "happy" mice with lower anxiety levels (Bravo et al., 2011). Other research has suggested that residents of the mammalian gastrointestinal tract influence asthma, autism, colitis, cancer, obesity, and diabetes. These findings are revolutionizing the way we think about microbes and could have exciting applications in humans.

Biotechnology is the application of organisms and their products to address human needs. We have used yeast and bacteria to ferment foods and beverages and improve crop health for millennia. Bacterial products are now found in household items and cosmetics and used in medical procedures. We use bacterial lipases and proteases as detergent additives and toxins like the botulinum toxin (known commercially as Botox) to reduce wrinkles. Furthermore, we use microbes as basic tools in bioengineering and chemical manufacturing. Human genes cloned into bacteria and yeast serve as pharmaceutical factories that produce valuable proteins, such as insulin (Slonczewski & Foster, 2011, p. 35). Bacteria can be used to break down pollutants and detoxify contaminated environments, a process known as bioremediation. In 2010, in the Gulf of Mexico, hydrocarbon-consuming microbes helped to degrade much of the Deepwater Horizon oil spill (Biello, 2010). Microbes can even help recycle elements trapped in landfill garbage and return them to the biosphere.

While a subset of microbes are pathogenic to humans, animals, or plants, the benefit we realize from the vast majority of microbes seems almost endless. In the following sections, we will learn about microbial compounds with pharmaceutical activity and the roles they may play in Nature.

References

Biello, D. (2010). Meet the microbes eating the gulf oil spill. Scientific American. August 18, 2010. <http://www.scientificamerican.com/article.cfm?id=gulf-oil-eating-microbes-slide-show>

Boucher, H. W., Talbot, G. H., Bradley, J. S., Edwards, J. E., Gilbert, D., Rice, L. B., Scheld, M., Spellberg, B., & Bartlett, J. (2009). Bad bugs, no drugs: no ESKAPE! An update from the Infectious Diseases Society of America. Clin Infect Dis 48:1-12.

Bravo, J. A., Forsythe, P., Chew, M. V., Escaravage, E., Savignac, H. M., Dinan, T. G., Bienenstock, J., & Cryan, J. F. (2011). Ingestion of Lactobacillus strain regulates emotional behavior and central GABA receptor expression in a mouse via the vagus nerve. Proc Natl Acad Sci U S A, 108:16050-16055. doi: 10.1073/pnas.1102999108.

Naik, S., Bouladoux, N., Wilhelm, C., Molloy, M. J., Salcedo, R., Kastenmuller, W., Deming, C., Quinones, M., Koo, L., Conlan, S., Spencer, S., Hall, J. A., Dzutsey, A., Kong, H., Campbell, D. J., Trinchieri, G., & Segre, J. A., Belkaid, Y. (2012). Compartmentalized control of skin immunity by resident commensals. Science, 337:1115-1119. doi: 10.1126/science.1225152.

Slonczewski, J., & Foster, J. W. (2011). *Microbiology: An Evolving Science* (2nd ed.). New York: W.W. Norton.

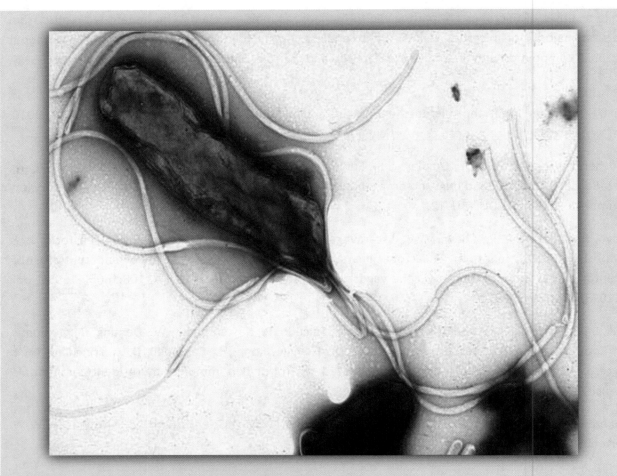

Figure 6-1. This electron micrograph shows *Helicobacter pylori*, a resident of the stomach, with multiple flagella that the bacterium uses to move in the mucous layer of the stomach lining. Photo source: commons. wikimedia.org.

Milestones in Microbiology

The Australian scientist Barry Marshall discovered that peptic ulcers and gastritis are caused by bacteria living in the stomach, which was generally believed to be too acidic for bacteria to survive. His inability to isolate and culture the bacterium, *Helicobacter pylori*, damaged his credibility in the scientific community and sustained commonly held myths about the stomach and ulcers. In a courageous effort to validate his findings, Marshall drank a culture of the infectious bacterium and developed symptoms of gastritis after a few days. An endoscopy and biopsy demonstrated that the bacterium was in fact present on the stomach lining, which was inflamed. After antibiotic treatment, the symptoms subsided, providing compelling evidence that the *H. pylori* was, in fact, the cause of ulcers. Marshall conducted the experiment in the 1980s and received the 2005 Nobel Prize for his work, which revolutionized views about the extreme conditions in which bacteria can grow, the assumption that all bacteria can be cultured, and the standard treatment for ulcers.

Experiment 6: Understand the significance of the ESKAPE pathogens and using safe relatives in the lab

Biological Questions:

- What ESKAPE pathogen do you wish to study?
- Why is your ESKAPE pathogen of choice a health concern?
- Are there any known antibiotics that are used to treat an infection caused by your ESKAPE pathogen?

Background:

Objective:

ESKAPE Pathogen of Choice:

Reasons for Choosing ESKAPE Pathogen:

General Cellular and Morphological Characteristics of the Organism:

Clinical Importance and Prevalence:

Infection (How does the infection occur and where is it localized?):

Pathology (What disease is caused? What are the symptoms?):

Ineffective Antibiotics (antibiotics to which the organism has acquired resistance):

Effective Antibiotics (antibiotics known to inhibit the organism):

Corresponding Safe Relative:

Notes:

Section 7:
Antibiotic Discovery, Structure, & Targets

The Father of Antibiotics

Alexander Fleming is famous as the "accidental" discoverer of **penicillin** – the first antibiotic, which revolutionized the world of medicine. But how "accidental" was his discovery really? Was Fleming really the first to observe this type of amazing microbial activity? In reality, this bacteriologist made his discovery because he already knew what he was looking for. Years of practice in his field had provided him with keen skills of observation and inquiry, enabling him to turn a small observation into a find with monumental implications.

Throughout the 1800s, highly corrosive **antiseptics** were being used to treat severe infections, especially those suffered by soldiers wounded in wars. These antiseptics were damaging to human tissue and the human immune system. Most casualties of war actually resulted from the infections and treatments given after the battles. Scientists and medical professionals referred to this situation as the **antiseptic dilemma**.

During the early 1900s, Fleming began his quest for an alternative to antiseptics – a chemical that could selectively kill bacteria without harming host cells. This idea resonated with Paul Ehrlich's **magic bullet** hypothesis, which stated that if certain chemicals, such as dyes, could selectively bind to specific bacteria, then there should be compounds that selectively inhibit growth as well. Ehrlich went on to develop the first human-made antimicrobial, salvarsan, in 1909. Salvarsan was effective in syphilis treatment but was later found to be too toxic for human use (Amyes, 2001), making it a great example of the antiseptic dilemma.

It was not until 1928 that Fleming came across his rather famous messy stack of plates awaiting disposal. As Fleming examined the plates, he noticed that one was contaminated. Moldy plates were not uncommon in the lab; however, there was something unique about this plate: *Staphylococcus* cells were not growing along the perimeter of the mold, forming a **zone of inhibition** (Fleming, 2001)! Fleming was intrigued by this observation and eventually showed that the zone of inhibition was caused by a compound that he named penicillin after the fungus that produces it, *Penicillium notatum*.

Characteristics of antibiotics:

- Therapeutic agents
- Selectively toxic toward microbes
- Generally antibacterial
- Small molecules (secondary metabolites)
- May be synthetic or natural products

To test the effectiveness of penicillin, Fleming performed various activity assays against common pathogens. Penicillin inhibited the growth of Gram-positive bacteria associated with scarlet fever, pneumonia, gonorrhea, meningitis, and strep throat while leaving eukaryotic cells unharmed (Brown, 2005). It exhibited the qualities of the miracle drug Fleming had been pursuing for years. However, he was unable to purify the compound in an active and stable form, making it impossible to test *in vivo*. He could not test penicillin in humans at concentrations that would reach and have impact at the site of infection without exposing test subjects to extraneous compounds also present in the mold culture.

Work on penicillin lay dormant for ten years until pharmacologist Howard Florey and biochemist Ernst Chain came across Fleming's paper. Their combined knowledge of chemistry allowed them to purify the active compound and test it on infectious bacteria *in vivo*, proving its therapeutic ability in humans (Amyes, 2001). Their work, coupled with the extraordinarily high-producing strain discovery by Mary Hunt and Kenneth Raper, enabled penicillin to be mass produced and administered to patients orally. Penicillin was commercialized in time to reach wounded soldiers in the battlefields of World War II and significantly contributed to the Allied victory and making World War II the first war in America's history in which more soldiers died of the direct effects of bullets and bombs than of infections. The collaborative development of the first natural product antibiotic won Fleming, Florey, and Chain the Nobel Prize in Physiology or Medicine in 1945.

From a Spoiled Cantaloupe in Peoria...

the best of 100,000 strains of Penicillium

Milestones in Microbiology

The development of penicillin led to a worldwide search for a strain of the *Penicillium* mold that would produce copious amounts of the antibiotic and grow in liquid culture. Mary Hunt (popularly known as Moldy Mary), a technician in the USDA lab in Peoria, Illinois run by Dr. Kenneth Raper, scoured produce in local markets in search of the strain and came across a moldy cantaloupe, whose cells produced the largest amount of penicillin when improved and grown in deep-vat, submerged conditions. This allowed the antibiotic to be mass-produced and sent to the battlefront of World War II.

Photo source: <http://www.peoriahistoricalsociety.org/!/Exhibits-PenicillinMoldyMary> Date accessed: July 21, 2014.

Milestones in Microbiology

It is worth noting that Fleming was not the first one to come across these observations. Texts from Ancient Egypt describe the use of moldy bread to treat postural eruptions on the scalp (Böttcher, 1959), while the Bible mentions the curative value of hyssop. It was on this plant (photo above) that the Swedish naturalist Westling found *Penicillium notatum* thousands of years later (Brown, 2005). Although Fleming himself coined the term "penicillin," an inscription on a therapeutic ointment with the word "PENICILLE," found in an Ancient Roman site, perplexed archeologists many years later after this drug became a common household name (Böttcher). Yet through all these years, people had exploited these molds for their curative value without understanding the chemistry and biology underpinning the effects. Many scientists attempted to uncover its inhibitory properties in the 1800s after Louis Pasteur discovered the role of bacteria in infection. Joseph Lister noticed that the *Penicillium* mold inhibited the reproduction of bacteria ten years before Fleming was born and, ten years after, another scientist attributed this inhibition to "the secretion of a specific substance," with no further clarification as to what was secreting it or what the substance was. French scientist Ernest Duchesne even injected the culture broth into mice infected with typhoid, and they were cured soon after. Nevertheless, none of these scientists identified the chemical and either did not provide conclusive information or gave up on their research.

This story is quite revealing about the importance of record keeping, serendipity, and persistence in discovery!

Photo source: commons.wikimedia.org.

Antibiotics

Penicillin was special due to its ability to kill bacteria without the toxic side effects of antiseptics, which lacked selectivity and harmed human and bacterial cells alike. In 1942, Selman Waksman coined the term "antibiotic" to describe any small molecule produced by a microbe that kills or inhibits the growth of other microbes (Clardy, Fischbach, & Currie, 2009). "Small molecules" refers to the fact that antibiotics are smaller than the macromolecules that constitute a cell. Antibiotics vary in their structures (Figure 7-1), falling into several chemical groups, or **classes**, of antibiotics. Entirely new classes of antibiotics are even more challenging to discover than new antibiotics themselves. A common class of antibiotics is the β-lactams, which share a four-member ring structure, which is the core of β-lactams like penicillin that enables them to inhibit cell wall synthesis (more on targets below) (Figure 7-1). One of the most recent classes of antibiotics was discovered in 2004, nearly 300 meters below the surface in the Sea of Japan. The antibiotic class was aptly named "abyssomicins" after the abyss of the deep ocean. These are polycyclic antibiotics produced by marine bacteria in the genus *Verrucosispora*. Abyssomicin C inhibits the growth of vancomycin- and methicillin-resistant *Staphylococcus aureus* by blocking their ability to produce folic acid (Nicolaou, Harrison, & Chen, 2009).

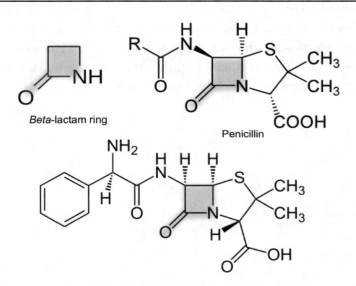

Beta-lactam ring

Penicillin

Ampicillin, a semi-synthetic derivative of penicillin

Figure 7-1. Members of the β-lactam class of antibiotics, such as penicillin and ampicillin, all share a common core structure: a four-member β-lactam ring. This structure makes β-lactam antibiotics able to inhibit bacterial cell wall synthesis.

Strictly speaking, true antibiotics are naturally occurring antimicrobial compounds, known as **natural products antibiotics**. This category of antimicrobials includes common drugs, such as penicillin, streptomycin, and chloramphenicol, which were originally isolated from living microorganisms. Natural product antibiotics make up 60-80% of all antimicrobials; the rest are generally synthetically derived from known chemical scaffolds and developed by chemists. Bacteria in the genus *Streptomyces* are the most prolific antibiotic producers known, as they produce 60% of all antibiotics in clinical use today.

Streptomyces are a perfect example of bacteria with virtuosic biosynthetic abilities that have changed the course of human history. They are also a perfect example of the potential for drug discovery.

Genome sequencing has revealed that many *Streptomyces* species contain dozens of "silent" pathways for antibiotic biosynthesis (Omura et al., 2001). These silent pathways comprise genes that are not expressed under lab conditions. By analyzing the sequences of silent pathways, scientists have been able to predict the compound they produce. Many researchers are now trying to unlock these pathways to enable the microorganisms to produce novel antibiotics. Some estimates suggest that humans have only discovered 0.1-10% of the natural products of bacteria, which is why the Small World Initiative is so exciting – this is the treasure trove we aim to discover!

Antibiotic Biosynthesis

Antibiotics can be classified based on their chemical structures, their cellular and molecular targets, or the bacterial cellular processes they inhibit. The structures and mode of synthesis are linked in interesting ways. Unlike many proteins, which are translated from messenger RNA to produce the final product, antibiotics are not directly encoded in DNA. Natural antibiotics are produced by complex **biosynthesis pathways**, stepwise chemical reactions catalyzed by enzymes within the cell. They may result from enzyme-catalyzed assembly and modification of amino acids, fatty acids, and sugars. For example, penicillin, a β-lactam antibiotic, is the product of three amino acids – cysteine, valine, and an amino acid intermediate: α-aminoadipate (Figure 7-2) (Clardy et al., 2009). Additionally, some of the enzymes involved in tetracycline (a polyketide antibiotic) and streptomycin (an aminoglycoside) biosynthesis are related to enzymes involved in fatty acid and polysaccharide synthesis, respectively (Clardy et al., 2009; Walsh, 2004). The degree to which these organic substituents are assembled and modified to form an antibiotic helps us group them based on shared chemical characteristics.

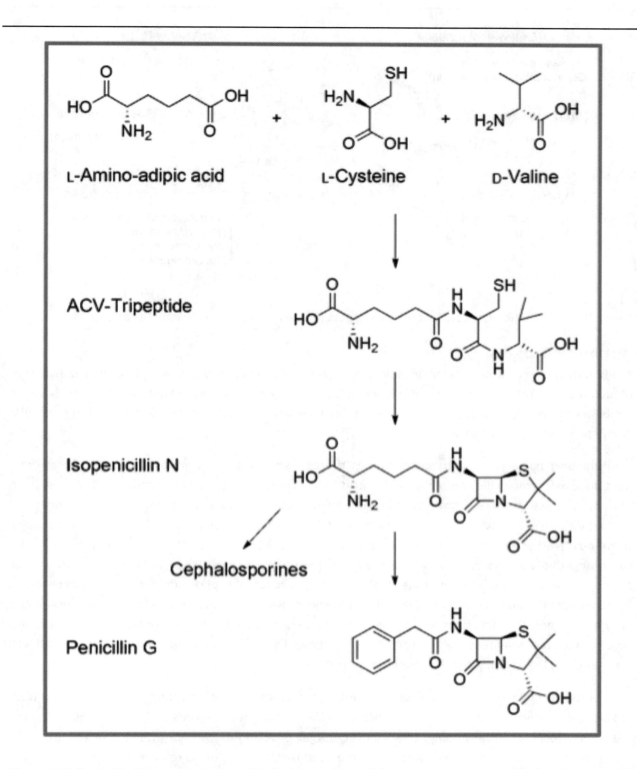

Figure 7-2. Penicillin biosynthesis. Penicillin is the product of three amino acids modified and assembled in an enzyme-catalyzed reaction. Photo source: commons.wikipedia.org (public domain).

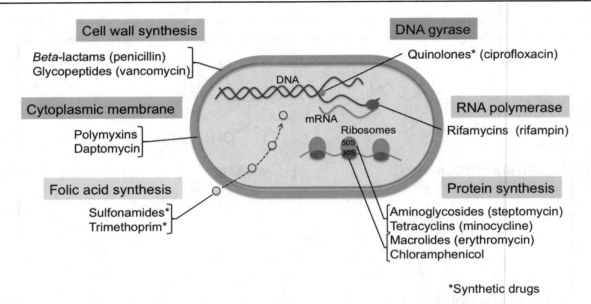

Figure 7-3. Schematic of antibiotic's cellular targets (modes of action) and examples of each.

Antibiotic Targets

Antibiotics with the same cellular or molecular target are also typically subdivided by their **mechanism of action**. This refers to the specific biochemical interaction that allows the antibiotic to have an inhibitory effect. The fact that antibiotics are selectively toxic to bacteria implies that the target cellular components are specific to bacteria.

One uniquely bacterial cellular component is the cell wall, which is composed of a polysaccharide-peptide (a macromolecule containing amino acids and a complex sugar) called **peptidoglycan**. This tough material protects bacteria from forces in the environment, such as changes in osmotic potential and mechanical force. It provides bacteria with structural support and gives them their characteristic shapes. **Gram-positive** bacteria have a thick peptidoglycan layer that is exposed to the environment, whereas **Gram-negative** bacteria have only a thin layer of peptidoglycan positioned between the cytoplasmic membrane and the outer membrane, which is composed of phospholipids and lipopolysaccharides. Some common antibiotics, including penicillin and vancomycin, inhibit cell wall synthesis by blocking the enzymes responsible for forming the peptide cross-links between peptidoglycan subunits. Growth requires constant maintenance and remodeling of the cell wall. When antibiotics interfere with cell wall maintenance, the growing cells will eventually burst (or lyse).

Translation (protein synthesis) is another cellular process that provides a target for antibiotics. Both eukaryotes and prokaryotes must synthesize proteins, and the mechanisms they use are quite similar, but their ribosomes differ enough to selectively target prokaryotes without affecting eukaryotic cells. Some antibiotics can bind to eukaryotic ribosomes, but they typically do so relatively weakly versus their observed binding to prokaryotic ribosomes. Antibiotics that target protein synthesis bind to one of three main ribosomal sites. Macrolides, such as erythromycin, bind to the E site in the 50S subunit of the ribosome, preventing ribosomal translocation. Other antibiotics, such as the aminoglycosides, bind to the A site on the 30S subunit, deforming the ribosome and interfering with codon-anticodon hydrogen bonding. Finally, some antibiotics bind to the peptidyl-transferase center (the P site) on the 50S subunit, inhibiting peptide bond formation.

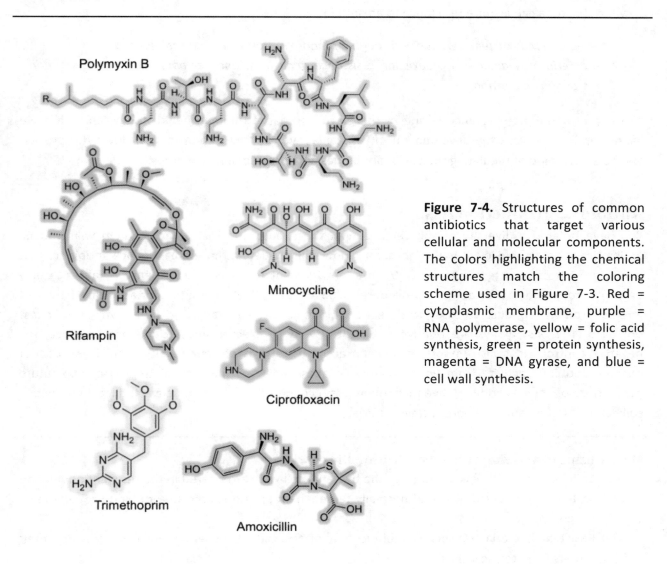

Figure 7-4. Structures of common antibiotics that target various cellular and molecular components. The colors highlighting the chemical structures match the coloring scheme used in Figure 7-3. Red = cytoplasmic membrane, purple = RNA polymerase, yellow = folic acid synthesis, green = protein synthesis, magenta = DNA gyrase, and blue = cell wall synthesis.

DNA metabolism also has some unique qualities in bacteria. The enzyme DNA gyrase has a similar structure in prokaryotes and eukaryotes, but antibiotics like ciprofloxacin take advantage of small differences in affinity to molecules. DNA gyrase aids in DNA replication by keeping the DNA molecule from overwinding and forming supercoils that block the DNA replication machinery from moving across the template. Similarly, rifampin inhibits RNA polymerase, which is necessary for transcription of the DNA code.

Antibiotics are effective because they exploit the cellular and molecular differences between bacteria and eukaryotes, specifically targeting necessary functions in bacterial cells. Many bacteria have, nevertheless, evolved mechanisms to counteract these compounds. There are two broad mechanisms by which bacteria can acquire resistance to an antibiotic:

1. *Bacteria may acquire resistance through a random mutation in a normal gene, or*
2. *Bacteria may acquire a preexisting resistance gene from another bacterium, most commonly through conjugation.*

The rise of antibiotic resistance is one of the biggest threats to human health today, and while we cannot entirely prevent the development of resistance, we can take action to slow down this process and do a better job of regulating the use of antibiotics while developing new drugs.

Antibiotic Production Assay

You have isolated a diversity of soil bacteria with the expectation that some of them will produce antibiotics at detectable levels in the laboratory. How will you detect those that produce antibiotics that inhibit growth of your test organism? When scientists want to assess the presence or absence of a particular component, they design a procedure called an "assay," which is a test for a specific activity of interest. You will conduct an assay to detect antibiotic activity by examining the growth of your test organism. The best assays are relatively straightforward to execute and include both positive and negative controls. It is also important to keep accurate records of your results even if you do not observe antibiotic activity from your isolates. Database analyses may reveal trends to help future generations of Small World Initiative team members recognize the most productive and least productive soil habitats to find antibiotic-producing bacteria.

Mechanisms of antibiotic resistance within the cell:
1. Cellular and molecular target (e.g., the bacterial cell wall) are altered in the resistant population so that antibiotics that would normally target them are no longer able to bind properly (e.g., vancomycin).
2. Resistant bacteria transport antibiotics out of the cell to prevent them from reaching their targets (e.g., tetracyclines).
3. The resistant bacterium may prevent the antibiotic from entering the cytoplasm (e.g., lantibiotics).
4. The antibiotic may be modified or destroyed by the resistant bacterium (e.g., β-lactams).

More on antibiotic resistance in Section 10.

References

Amyes, S. G. B. (2001). *Magic Bullets, Lost Horizons: The Rise and Fall of Antibiotics*. New York: Taylor & Francis.

Böttcher, H. H. (1959). *Miracle Drugs*. London: Heinemann.

Brown, K. (2005). *Penicillin Man: Alexander Fleming and the Antibiotic Revolution*. Stroud, Gloucestershire: Sutton.

Clardy, J., Fischbach, M. A., & Currie, C. R. (2009). The natural history of antibiotics. Curr Biol, 19:R437-R441. doi: 10.1016/j.cub.2009.04.001.

Nicolaou, K. C., Harrison, S. T., & Chen, J. S. (2009). Discoveries from the abyss: the abyssomicins and their total synthesis. Synthesis (Stuttg), 2009:33-42. doi: 10.1055/s-0028-1083259.

Omura, S., Ikeda, H., Ishikawa, J., Hanamoto, A., Takahashi, C., Shinose, M., Takahashi, Y., Horikawa, H., Nakazawa, H., Osonoe, T., Kikuchi, H., Shiba, T., Sakaki, Y., & Hattori, M. (2001). Genome sequence of an industrial microorganism *Streptomyces avermitilis*: deducing the ability of producing secondary metabolites. Proc Natl Acad Sci U S A, 98:12215-12220. doi: 10.1073/pnas.211433198.

Walsh, C. T. (2004). Polyketide and nonribosomal peptide antibiotics: modularity and versatility. Science, 303:1805-1810. doi: 10.1126/science.1094318.

Other sources:

Butler, M. S., & Buss, A. D. (2006). Natural products – the future scaffolds for novel antibiotics? Biochem Pharmacol, 71:919-929. doi: http://dx.doi.org/10.1016/j.bcp.2005.10.012.

D'Costa, V. M., Griffiths, E., & Wright, G. D. (2007). Expanding the soil antibiotic resistome: exploring environmental diversity. Curr Opin Microbiol, 10:481-489. doi: 10.1016/j.mib.2007.08.009.

Harvey, A. (2000). Strategies for discovering drugs from previously unexplored natural products. Drug Discov Today, 5:294-300.

Linares, J. F., Gustafsson, I., Baquero, F., & Martinez, J. L. (2006). Antibiotics as intermicrobial signaling agents instead of weapons. Proc Natl Acad Sci U S A, 103:19484-19489. doi: 10.1073/pnas.0608949103.

Watve, M. G., Tickoo, R., Jog, M. M., & Bhole, B. D. (2001). How many antibiotics are produced by the genus *Streptomyces*? Arch Microbiol, 176:386-390. doi: 10.1007/s002030100345.

Experiment 7: Design a method to screen for antibiotic producers

Biological Questions:
- How will you determine whether your soil isolates produce antibiotics?
- What positive and negative controls will you use in your assays?
- What factors influence antibiotic production in a microorganism?
- Can we increase the antibiotic yield of our isolates?

Background:

Objective:

Hypothesis and rationale:

Experimental design and protocols used:

Controls and treatments:

Data and observations:

Interpretations and conclusions:

Notes:

Assignment: Calculating Frequency of Antibiotic Producers

Objective:

Tester organism:

Tester organism media:

Results:

Sample:	Calculating frequency (%)		
Medium for isolation	Number of patches	Isolates producing antibiotic (number)	Isolates producing antibiotics (%)
Total			

Calculations:

Comments:

Notes:

Don't forget to update your entry and include your data in the Small World Initiative Soil Sample Database: *www.smallworldinitiative.org/data*

Section 8: Getting to Know Your Isolates

As we experience the thrill of isolating microbes that produce antibiotic compounds, it is an appropriate time to reflect on our accomplishments thus far and to consider the future direction of our research. Starting with soil samples containing a high density of bacteria, we have isolated microbes capable of inhibiting organisms related to known pathogens. Furthermore, we have demonstrated that the antibiotic producers are capable of growing in isolation (away from the community of microbes inhabiting the soil) and under laboratory conditions – important traits required for mass production of an antibiotic. But what's next?

We must emphasize that it is a long journey from initial discovery to mass market. There are many criteria that must be met for a new antibiotic to be successful commercially. Vast amounts of compound are required; toxicity to humans must be minimal at an effective treatment dose; compounds that remain active after oral ingestion (i.e., in pill form) are more desirable than compounds requiring intravenous administration; and so on. A first step in addressing these issues requires isolation of the active compound in pure form. We learned from Fleming's work that this can be a challenge. Separation of the active compound from all of the other compounds produced by the organism requires expensive equipment and often takes years of work for even the most experienced chemists. For this reason, scientists place high value on steps that help to identify, early on, whether the active compound is likely to be new or is a previously identified molecule. We will discuss the chemical purification and identification process in Section 9 and Future Directions.

Concurrent with chemical purification, another approach that lends insight into the potential identity of the unknown molecule is characterization of the producing microbe. For example, *Acremonium chrysogenum* is known to produce cephalosporin C (a β-lactam). If an active soil isolate can be classified as *Acremonium* or a close relative, a priority would be to determine whether the active compound exhibits chemical properties of the cephalosporins.

Classifying Microbes

Taxonomy is the field of biology concerned with naming and organizing living organisms into meaningful groups based on similar characteristics. Groups with shared physical features often (but not always) share an evolutionary history. Historically, scientists classified microbes by observing morphological features under the microscope and through biochemical (metabolic) assays that could determine the presence of specific enzymes. In the late 20th century, the development of technologies for comparing DNA sequences provided biologists with a more meaningful approach to classification and thus gained widespread appeal. Nucleotide sequence similarity provides a way to assess evolutionary relatedness. After all, mutations (heritable changes in the DNA sequence) are the underlying molecular basis for Darwin's "descent with modification." Although whole genome comparisons are now possible, a bacterial genome may consist of several million base pairs – far too many for quick, routine comparisons. For this reason, scientists typically compare sequences of established "marker genes," those that are present in all microbes and for which function has been conserved. By far, the most commonly used marker gene encodes a small ribosomal subunit (SSU) RNA, the 16S rRNA gene (18S rRNA gene in eukaryotes). 16S rRNA gene comparisons are performed routinely today, but they still do not entirely replace morphological analysis (when possible). It is important to remember that the strongest taxonomic identifications involve a wide range of techniques, so the results from one method can validate another method. We discuss morphological and molecular taxonomic classification methods in this section and biochemical classification in Section 11.

Molecular Phylogeny

Use of the 16S rRNA gene as a tool for comparing microbes was first proposed by Carl Woese and George Fox in 1977 (Woese and Fox, 1977). At that time, classification of multicellular organisms relied on readily observable morphological features, a system that is not easily applied to microbes. Frustrated by the challenges in determining evolutionary relationships among organisms with unimpressive fossil records and few distinguishing visible differences, Woese and Fox searched for a new metric. The idea of using DNA sequences was revolutionary. One feature that makes DNA sequence comparison so valuable is that all living creatures use DNA as their heritable material. Furthermore, all organisms share homologous versions of the SSU genes. For the first time, scientists had a single marker with which to compare the relationships among all living creatures. This resulted in a dramatic rearrangement of what we call the universal tree of life. Comparing 16S and 18S rRNA gene sequences revealed that life is organized in three domains – Archaea, Bacteria, and Eukarya. The discovery that Archaea, although morphologically similar to Bacteria, were as different from Bacteria as Eukaryotes, along with the prevalence and diversity of microbes revealed by molecular phylogeny, stunned the scientific world.

Phylogenetic trees are hypotheses regarding the evolutionary relationships between taxonomic groups; some trees are constructed using SSU sequence data only while others take all available data into consideration. For this reason, trees for the same taxonomic groups may differ (although usually only slightly) depending on the criteria used for constructing the tree. The universal tree of life is based on what we call **molecular phylogeny**, meaning that the relationships presented are based on comparison of molecular features, usually DNA sequence, rather than morphological traits. Increasingly, DNA sequences are used in the construction of trees, but morphological data are still an important piece of the complete puzzle when making predictions about evolutionary relationships.

Other genes can serve as markers for comparison, but the 16S rRNA gene remains the gold standard for initial classification. There are many features that make the SSU gene a good yardstick, including its effectively universal presence and convenient size of about 1500 nucleotides; however, its most important advantage over other similar genes is that it contains regions of relatively high variability interspersed among other highly conserved regions. Comparison of the hypervariable regions is useful for identification since these regions typically contain nucleotide sequences that are unique to a particular species.

Phylogenetic Tree of Life

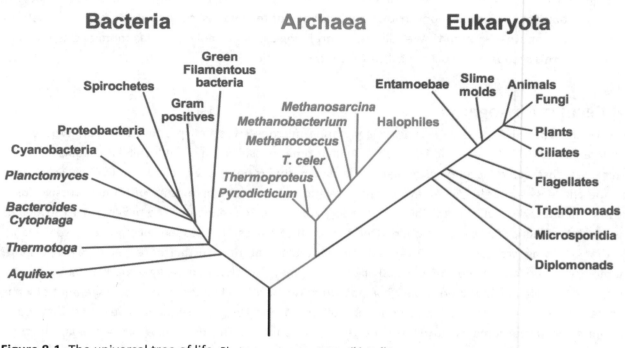

Figure 8-1. The universal tree of life. Photo source: commons.wikimedia.org.

Therefore, while SSU sequence comparisons were initially used to create phylogenetic trees for understanding the evolutionary history of life, 16S rRNA gene analysis is now routinely used to make preliminary hypotheses about the identity of unknown bacterial isolates. This is possible because of the vast collection of known 16S rRNA gene sequences in a publicly available database called GenBank. Search algorithms, such as BLAST, compare an input sequence to millions of known sequences in the database. Once closely matching database sequences are found, we can make a preliminary assumption that the unknown falls within the same taxonomic group as the known organisms with highly similar sequences (assuming that the highly similar sequences were themselves reliably identified). More definitive taxonomic assignment can be obtained from observing multiple molecular markers and morphological traits. We will use 16S rRNA gene sequence analysis to make a preliminary identification of our unknown organisms and to make predictions about whether our active molecules are novel.

Obtaining 16S rRNA Gene Sequence Data

DNA sequencing technology has advanced significantly in the past decade; there are now several methods to obtain a DNA sequence for a particular gene or genome. Common to all methods, however, is the requirement for many copies of the DNA destined for sequence analysis (the template). Polymerase chain reaction (PCR) is the technique most commonly employed to amplify (make copies of) the region to be sequenced. We can design PCR primers that are complementary to highly conserved regions of the 16S rRNA gene, thus allowing the same primers to bind to the DNA of a broad range of organisms. Because the amplification products will include the hypervariable regions located between these conserved sites, species-specific sequence data can be obtained for identification and classification purposes.

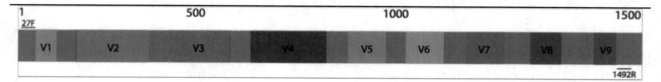

Figure 8-2. 16S rRNA gene illustrating the variable and conserved regions. "V" indicates variable regions, which are segments of the gene that show considerable sequence diversity between species. Gray boxes are the conserved regions. Conserved regions are more similar between organisms as these are the regions of the gene that are essential for translation or interact with ribosomal proteins. The conserved regions provide sequences for primers (in our case, 27F and 1492R) that bind to conserved regions to amplify and read all variable regions between the primer set; these are used for PCR and sequencing.

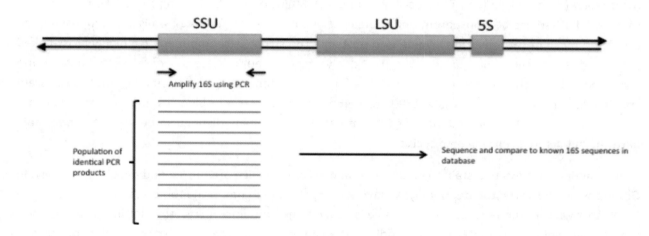

Figure 8-3. Diagrammatic representation of 16S rRNA gene amplification from the prokaryotic chromosome. The small subunit of the bacterial ribosome is encoded by the 16S rRNA gene (SSU), whereas the large subunit is encoded by the 23S rRNA gene (LSU) and the 5S rRNA gene (5S). Schematic adapted from Woese and Fox, 1977.

Morphological Characterization of Isolates

As mentioned, 16S rRNA gene sequence data are exceptionally useful for assigning preliminary taxonomic placement of an organism, but the tentative molecular identification is strengthened through use of several methods, usually executed simultaneously. Below, we introduce microscopy as a method to identify key morphological features. Biochemical (metabolic) tests also make up a facet of the identification tools available and will be discussed in Section 11.

Microbes Under the Microscope

The pioneers of microscopy in the late 15th century were also pioneers in the field of biology. Their development of powerful lenses allowed them to delve deeper into the microscopic world of unicellular organisms. Robert Hooke, a renowned Englishman who specialized in the sciences and architecture, is credited with the invention of the compound microscope with which he made detailed observations that are compiled in the book, *Micrographia*, published in 1665, which became a scientific bestseller. The book is famous for its detailed drawings of a fly's eye and the plant cells in a slice of cork. Hooke coined the term "cell" as the cork cell walls reminded him of the cells in monasteries.

Microscopy has come a long way from the time of the first microbial visualizations. Yet there are limitations to light microscopy, which can only resolve objects that are more than 0.2 μm (a μm is 1×10^{-6} meter, or a micron) apart. More advanced techniques, such as electron microscopy, discern even smaller structures, such as viruses and subcellular components. This technique produces images with incredible detail, resolving objects as close as 0.005 μm.

Staining the Bacterial Cell Wall

Staining enhances our ability to see the shapes of bacterial cells. Bacteria can be of many different shapes, but the most commonly observed are spherical (called cocci (plural) or coccus (singular)) and rod-shaped (called bacilli (plural) or bacillus (singular)). Stains do this by binding to cellular components that would otherwise be transparent under the light microscope. Bacterial cell walls are composed of an organized mesh of carbohydrates, lipids, and proteins. The structural component is a highly cross-linked polymer of sugar and amino acids called peptidoglycan. The peptidoglycan layer protects bacteria and gives them their characteristic shapes. One of the most famous classical staining methods, Gram staining, was developed in the late 1800s to help visualize bacteria in biopsies and has since become crucial for the classification and identification of bacteria by helping distinguish between the two main patterns of bacterial cell wall architecture.

Gram staining employs two stains, crystal violet and safranin, which are purple and pink, respectively. In Gram-positive bacteria, the peptidoglycan layer is very thick (>20 nm, or nanometers) and serves as the outermost wall component. Gram-positive cells retain large amounts of crystal violet in this layer. Once the crystal violet is complexed with iodine, the stains are better able to resist alcohol-acetone decolorization than in Gram-negative bacteria. As a result, Gram-positive cells are left with a purple appearance even after counterstaining with safranin. Conversely, in Gram-negative bacteria, the peptidoglycan layer is thin (normally <10 nm) and covered by an outer membrane. Because the peptidoglycan is so thin, Gram-negative walls are more susceptible to alcohol-acetone decolorization and are rendered colorless when washed with the alcohol-acetone solution. The decolorized cells will thus be left appearing pink once the safranin counterstain has been applied. By discriminating between Gram-positive and Gram-negative cells on a microscope slide, clinical personnel and microbiologists can deduce much information about an isolate's physiology. Furthermore, Gram staining provides an initial broad division that can be used to help classify bacteria. Gram-positives and Gram-negatives make up the two major groups of bacteria, which are generally representative of their evolutionary lineages. Therefore, Gram staining, although a classical method, is still widely used in both clinical and research microbiology to differentiate bacteria and serves as a preliminary method of characterization.

References

Woese, C. R., & Fox, G. E. (1977). Phylogenetic structure of the prokaryotic domain: The primary kingdoms. Proc Natl Acad Sci U S A 74:5088-5090.

Milestones in Microbiology

Hooke's work inspired a Dutchman who is often called "the father of microbiology," Antonie van Leeuwenhoek. Leeuwenhoek, who was known for his keen eyesight and lens-making skills, worked as a draper, which required the use of magnifying glasses to count the number of threads in fabrics. After reading *Micrographia* and combining his knowledge of lens-making with Hooke's techniques, Leeuwenhoek devised powerful single-lens microscopes, which may have had magnification powers between 200× and 500×. He was very secretive about his techniques and fewer than ten of his microscopes remain. He was such an advanced inventor that it took more than 150 years for scientists to develop microscopes as powerful as Leeuwenhoek's! He was the first to observe and document unicellular organisms, such as bacteria and protists, which he described as "wee animalcules." He famously observed the plaque between his own teeth and found that it contained hundreds of bacteria shaped like rods and spheres. Leeuwenhoek frequently sent letters to the Royal Society in London with detailed records of his findings, some of which are so detailed that they allow us to identify some of the species he observed with his microscopes. Source: University of California Museum of Paleontology – website: <http://www.ucmp.berkeley.edu/history/leeuwenhoek.html> Date accessed: 2 November 2013.

Leeuwenhoek's first representation of the "wee animalcules" he observed under the microscope. This is believed to be the first drawing of a bacterium.

Experiment 8: Conduct initial identification of your antibiotic-producing isolate

Biological Questions:
- What do you wish to know about your antibiotic producers?
- Can we identify bacteria based on their macroscopic morphologies? Why or why not?
- What cellular and molecular components in our isolates can give us the most information about their identities?
- How do we confirm what we learn about our isolates?

Background:

Objective:

Results:

Isolate name	Tentative genus	Closest relative (% identity)	Size of query sequence (nt)	Date of BLAST analysis	Gram stain	Cell shape	Antibiotics production	Other

Based on morphological and/or molecular data, indicate the number of distinct antibiotic producers:

Literature search:

- Morphology: Do your observations match information in the literature?

- Antibiotic production: Do your observations match information in the literature?

Interpretations and conclusions:

Notes:

Don't forget to update your entry and include your data in the Small World Initiative Soil Sample Database: *www.smallworldinitiative.org/data*

Section 9:
It All Comes Down to Chemistry

Life is a Collection of Chemicals

Just as organisms are composed of cells, cells are composed of organic molecules. Organic chemistry is the chemistry of compounds containing carbon. It is one of the foundational sciences of the pharmaceutical, perfumery, flavor, dyestuff, and materials industries and a vital part of modern biology. Some organic compounds are large, or macromolecules, such as proteins, nucleic acids, and fatty acids, and others are small, such as sugars, amino acids, organic acids, and nucleotides. Some small molecules are used as the starting material to build macromolecules; for example, amino acids are strung together to make proteins, and long chains of nucleotides make up DNA. But some small organic molecules have functions in their singular form.

The chemical reactions in cells that process molecules are called metabolism. Some of these reactions, known as primary metabolism, create the core functions of life – storing energy, releasing energy, and building macromolecules. In contrast, secondary metabolism creates molecules that are found in only a few organisms and are typically not essential for life. Some secondary metabolites are known to provide the producing organism with a selective advantage, but many are of unknown function.

Humans have taken advantage of secondary metabolites from plants, animals, and microorganisms for our own purposes. For example, the plant compound, indigo, is used as a dye, a snake venom is used to treat high blood pressure, and digoxin from the foxglove plant is a cardiac drug. For our studies, the most important classes of secondary metabolites are the antibiotics from microorganisms. Molecules of many chemical classes act as antibiotics, making microorganisms the most virtuosic chemists on earth. Some of the key classes of antibiotics are the β-lactams, such as penicillin; the polyketides, such as erythromycin; and the aminoglycosides, such as kanamycin (Figure 9-1).

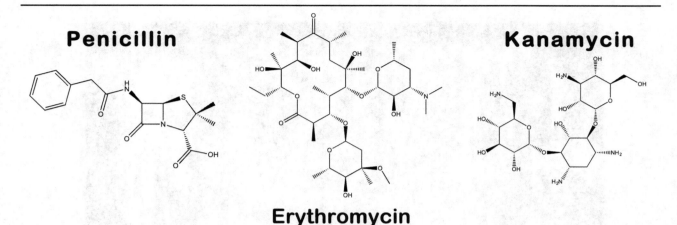

Figure 9-1. [From Left] Chemical structures of penicillin, erythromycin, and kanamycin. Image source: drawn by Nam Kim.

Isolation of Secondary Metabolites

Bacterial cultures contain a complex mixture of metabolites that were either in the medium used to grow the microorganism or were produced by the microorganism during growth. Therefore, the challenge with purifying an antibiotic is separating it from all the other metabolites in the culture. The process usually entails a series of separation steps based on the chemical and physical properties of the desired compound. For example, many methods separate compounds based on their relative polarity as indicated by the degree of interaction with various solvents. Polarity is measured by solubility in water or other solvents and is conferred by a partial charge on the molecule. Very polar compounds are soluble in water (sugar, for example), and non-polar compounds are not (oils, for example) and will dissolve better in non-polar solvents such as hexane. Molecules that are chemically similar to the active compound will be the most difficult to separate.

To isolate the compound responsible for antibiotic activity observed in the patch plates, we need to employ separation techniques that are based on characteristics, such as size, polarity, solubility, or affinity for certain types of surfaces. A good first step in purification is a simple solvent separation, using a solvent in which most primary metabolites (sugars and amino acids) are not soluble.

Milestones in Microbiology

Dorothy Crowfoot Hodgkin, a British chemist, advanced the technique of X-ray crystallography, a critical method to determine the 3D structures of biomolecules. She solved the structure of penicillin and demonstrated that it contains a β-lactam ring. Hodgkin also solved the structure of vitamin B_{12}, which led to the Nobel Prize in Chemistry in 1964. Britain's Royal Society celebrated their 350th anniversary with a set of commemorative stamps, one of which was of Hodgkin and her vitamin B_{12} molecule.

Solubility of Common Compounds

Dissolves well in water	Does not dissolve well in water

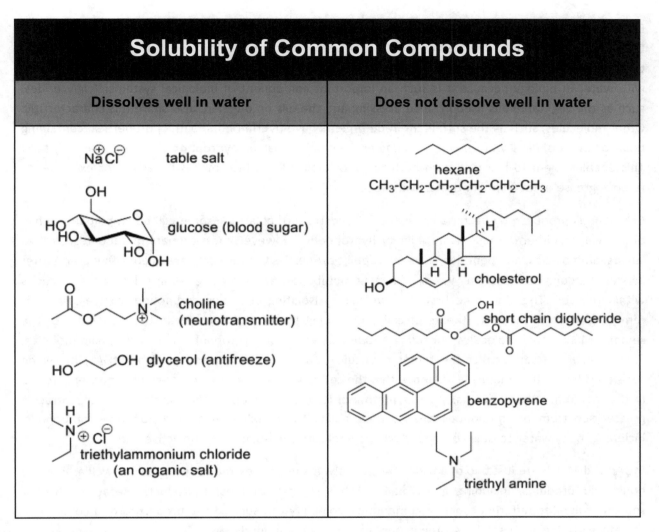

Extracting with Organic Solvents

While the process of chemical separation to isolate compounds may seem new, similar phenomena surround us. For example, salad dressings demonstrate that oil and vinegar do not mix and form separate layers with different densities and chemical properties. These two liquids also feel very different to our skins. Oil sticks while vinegar and other water-based solutions wash off easily. These familiar interactions are the result of a chemical property known as **polarity**.

Polarity defines the distribution of electron density and charge in a molecule. It results from the tendency of certain atoms to hold onto their shared electrons more closely than other atoms in a bond due to differences in electronegativity. These differences cause some molecules to have "poles" with partially opposing charges; we call these molecules "polar." Water (H_2O) is a great example. Each water molecule has a partial negative charge on the oxygen and partial positive charges on the hydrogen atoms. Atoms in molecules that exhibit this separation of electron density, like other water molecules and water-soluble compounds, will be attracted to other atoms of opposite charges in other polar molecules. These bonds are weak compared with covalent bonds but are strong enough to pull and solubilize polar molecules in a sample. Less polar molecules, such as **ethyl acetate** (CH_3-COO-CH_2-CH_3 or

EtOAc) separate from water due to the differences in polarity (similar to oil and water). Even though EtOAc has a "pole" with the carbonyl group (C=O) within its structure, it is not strong enough to "want" to be associated with water due to the methyl (CH₃) and ethyl (CH₃CH₂) groups. We focus on interaction with water in biology because it is such an important component of biological systems. Triglycerides, such as the vegetable oils used in salad dressing and the oils on our skin, also share this characteristic. Other molecules, such as the surfactant in detergents have hybrid (amphipathic) properties, containing polar or **hydrophilic** ("water-loving") heads and long nonpolar or **hydrophobic** ("water-fearing") tails. This enables them to mix well with both types of molecules, which makes it easier, for example, to remove grease or fat from our dishes with water.

Compounds produced by bacteria cover the full spectrum of polarity – some will be amphipathic while others will be either strongly hydrophilic or hydrophobic. However, most primary metabolites, such as sugars, amino acids, and peptides, have hydrophilic properties because cells are filled with water. Water acts as the "universal solvent" in cells, keeping metabolites and ionic species in solution for reactions within the cell. Therefore, the first step we use in isolating an active compound from a sample is removing most of the constituents of cells and seeing if we retain activity in the remainder of the sample. Many small molecules, including antibiotics, will have hydrophobic and hydrophilic moieties. Therefore, if we can extract the target molecule in a less polar solvent, such as EtOAc, it will be separated from other molecules found within the cell as well as from the water-soluble nutrients found in the medium. Other solvents, such as **methanol** (CH₃-OH or MeOH), the simplest alcohol, extract a greater spectrum of compounds due to their ability to solubilize polar and nonpolar compounds, including many water-soluble compounds that complicate the isolation of the active one.

EtOAc and MeOH are just two of a wide range of solvents used in extraction protocols as well as in many household products, including glues, nail polish removers, and paint products. Because different solvents solubilize different types of compounds, solubility can suggest the properties of a compound, therefore serving as a useful first step in purification of a compound.

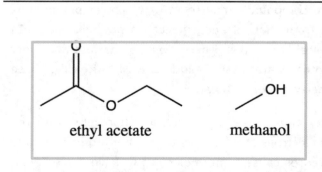

ethyl acetate   methanol

Figure 9-2. [Left] Molecular structure of ethyl acetate. This organic compound is nonpolar and serves as a common solvent for other organic, nonpolar compounds. **[Right]** Molecular structure of methanol. This compound contains a polar alcohol functional group (-OH), giving it hydrophilic properties. However, its methyl (-CH₃) group, which is slightly hydrophobic, allows it to solubilize both polar and nonpolar compounds to various degrees.

References

Clayden, J., Greeves, N., Warren, S., & Wothers, P. (2007). *Organic Chemistry,* New York: Oxford University Press, 2007.

Experiment 9: Test an organic extract of your isolate for antibiotic activity

Biological Questions:
- Can we isolate an antibiotic from a bacterial isolate? How?
- What does the choice of solvent for extraction assume about the chemical properties of the antibiotic compound?
- How can we assess whether the antibiotic is present in the extract?
- What else do we need to learn about the observed antibiotic activity?
- How will you proceed to study your antibiotic extract?

Background:

Objective:

Hypothesis and rationale:

Experimental design and protocols used:

Solvents used:

Solvent pros and cons:

Controls and treatments:

Data and observations:

Interpretations and conclusions:

Future directions:

Notes:

Don't forget to update your entry and include your data in the Small World Initiative Soil Sample Database: _www.smallworldinitiative.org/data_

Section 10: Resisting Antibiotics

The antibiotic crisis stems from the increasing prevalence of infectious organisms that fail to respond to treatment with conventional antibiotics, requiring clinicians to prescribe other antibiotics. Occasionally, clinicians have to resort to administering "last resort" antibiotics, which are reserved for the most recalcitrant infections. By the time these antibiotics are deployed, the infection may have spread and made the patient extremely ill and at risk of death. In the worst cases, the infectious organism is resistant to every antibiotic administered. The main reason that the ESKAPE pathogens are such a health threat is not that they, on their own, are particularly virulent; rather, it is the fact that these organisms represent the vast majority of antibiotic-resistant isolates that confound physicians in affected patients. In today's world, it is the acquisition of antibiotic resistance that renders treatment of bacterial infections challenging.

How Does Antibiotic Resistance Arise?

To understand antibiotic resistance, it is helpful to refer back to the mechanism of action of antibiotics and the molecular interactions that occur in cells. An antibiotic is a molecule that enters a cell and interacts with a target molecule; for example, antibiotics that bind to the prokaryotic ribosome have an inhibitory effect on protein synthesis. Any cellular change that prevents the antibiotic from reaching or binding to its target confers resistance to the organism.

There are two main mechanisms through which resistance is acquired. One involves mutations and the other involves acquisition of fragments of DNA harboring genes that confer resistance. Bacteria can acquire DNA from other cells, from the environment (released from lysed cells for example), or from viruses through a process called **horizontal gene transfer** (**HGT**). We use the term "horizontal" to distinguish this from the traditional "vertical" transfer of DNA that occurs when a bacterial cell undergoes fission and passes its gene on to a daughter cell. Examples of resistance gene sets acquired through HGT are genes that code for pumps that expel antibiotics from the cell or enzymes that chemically modify antibiotics, thereby inactivating them (i.e., they are no longer able to reach or bind to their targets).

Specific mutations that arise through errors in DNA replication can also lead to resistance if: (a) the mutation alters the structure of an antibiotic target such that the binding affinity of the antibiotic is decreased and (b) the function of the target is still retained. Remember that antibiotics target structures or functions that are essential for the life of the organism, so only certain mutations meet these criteria.

Antibiotic Resistance in the Environment

When there is selective pressure to maintain the change to the genome, regardless of the mechanism resulting in the change, a resistant population of cells can arise. This can occur in microbes proliferating within patients taking antibiotics to fight infections; from there, resistant bacteria present in feces and bodily fluids can contaminate household or hospital surfaces. Antibiotic-resistant bacteria can spread in the environment through waste disposal, and the use of antibiotics as growth-promoting agents in livestock feed provides further selection pressure for survival of resistant organisms. More than 50% of antibiotics sold in the United States, for example, are used in livestock production, which has become a topic of contentious debate (Figure 10-1).

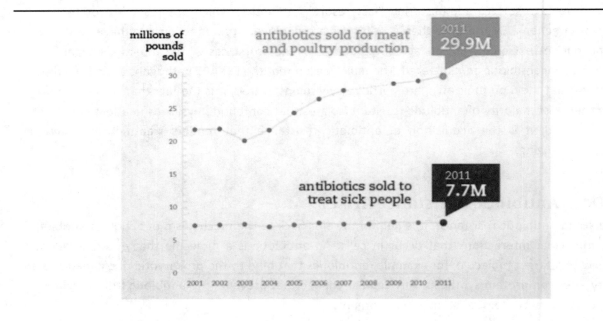

Figure 10-1. U.S. sales of antibiotics, 2001–2011. Photo source: Pew Charitable Trusts http://www.pewhealth.org/other-resource/record-high-antibiotic-sales-for-meat-and-poultry-production-85899449119.

Antibiotic use by humans is relatively recent in the history of evolution of life, but antibiotics have been produced by microbes in their natural environments for millennia. The natural role of these compounds is currently unknown, but we can be certain the intended function is not to cure humans of infectious disease. Antibiotics may be one of the most ancient forms of biological warfare. Perhaps secretion of antibiotics is a mechanism employed by microbes to compete with neighboring microbes for limited resources. And as usually occurs in nature, those neighbors that survived the onslaught of antimicrobial compounds proliferated, thus passing on their resistance determinants to subsequent populations of cells either through vertical or horizontal transmission. However, there are only a few known examples to support this notion. Alternatively, resistance genes have been speculated to protect microbes from toxins secreted by plants and insects, and antibiotics have been proposed to play a role in cell-cell signaling. The natural role of most antibiotics remains unknown and the subject of active research.

What we do know is that resistant microbes are frequently detected soon after the introduction of an antibiotic for clinical use (Figure 10-2). Surprisingly, this trend proves true even for compounds synthesized only in the lab, for which there has not been selection pressure for resistance in evolutionary history. This highlights the need for more prudent antibiotic use and for the ongoing discovery of new compounds.

In the context of our own research, we might ask whether those microbes that produce antibiotics are likely to harbor antibiotic resistance determinants. It may seem logical that a microbe would be resistant to an antibiotic that it produces. But how likely is it to be resistant to other antibiotics? And how prevalent is resistance in the environment in the absence of known selective pressure? One important feature in the rapid spread of antibiotic resistance is the fact that antibiotic resistance genes tend to cluster within the same region of the bacterial chromosome, such that HGT often results in acquisition of resistance to many antibiotics even in the absence of selective pressure for many of the resistance genes.

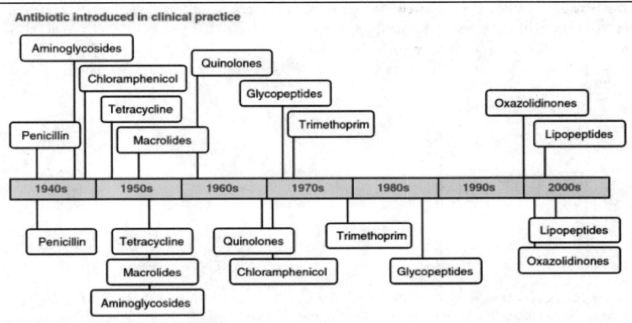

Figure 10-2. Timeline of introduction and appearance of resistance to various antibiotics.

Photo source: Högberg, D. L., Heddini, A., Cars, O. (2010). The global need for effective antibiotics: challenges and recent advances. Trends Pharmacol Sci, 31:509-515.

Fighting Antibiotic Resistance

The prevalence of antibiotic resistance has called for the exploration of new antibiotics and also for the modification of existing antibiotics. At the time of its discovery, penicillin could easily treat a *Staphylococcus aureus* skin infection. As the bacterium acquired resistance, alternatives needed to be developed. In 1959, methicillin was introduced as an alternative to penicillin. Methicillin is a penicillin derivative, which is insensitive to enzymes that would normally break down β-lactams (β-lactamases). Yet within years of its introduction, resistance was observed. The number of reported cases of methicillin-resistant *S. aureus* (MRSA) has been growing rapidly over the last two decades (Figure 10-3). The last resort antibiotic, vancomycin, has come into common use to treat infections by multidrug-resistant bacteria, and the synthetic antibiotic zylox is now used to treat even more serious infections that are no longer sensitive to vancomycin (Figure 10-4).

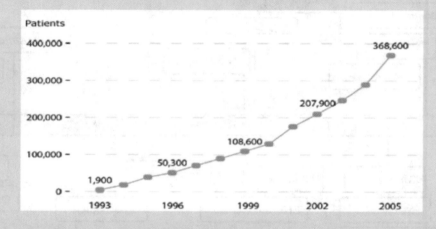

Figure 10-3. Cases of methicillin-resistant *Staphylococcus aureus* (MRSA) annually in the United States. Adapted from "Hospital stays with MRSA infections 1993-2005." Source: AHRQ, Center for Delivery, Organization and Markets, Healthcare Cost and Utilization Project, Nationwide Inpatient Sample, 1993-2005.

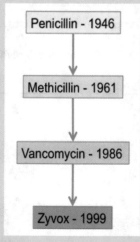

Figure 10-4. The introduction of alternatives to penicillin to treat *Staphylococcus* infections. Adapted from Palumbi, S. (2001) Humans as the world's greatest evolutionary force. Science, 293:1786-1790.

References

Allen, H. K., Donato, J., Wang, H. H., Cloud-Hansen, K. A., Davies, J., & Handelsman, J. (2010). Call of the wild: Antibiotic resistance genes in natural environments. Nat Rev Microbiol, 8:251-259.

Davies, J., & Davies, D. (2010). Origins and evolution of antibiotic resistance. Microbiol Mol Biol Rev, 74:417-433. doi: 10.1128/Mmbr.00016-10.

Rice, L. B. (2010). Progress and challenges in implementing the research on ESKAPE pathogens. Infect Control Hosp Epidemiol, 31: S7-S10.

Experiment 10: Test your isolate's resistance to common antibiotics

Biological Questions:

- Are the antibiotic-producing isolates sensitive to known antibiotics?
- If so, what does this tell us about the isolates? How might this relate to the antibiotics they produce?

Background:

Objective:

Hypothesis and rationale:

Experimental design and protocols used:

Controls and treatments:

Data and observations:

Isolate ID	Antibiotic tested	Mechanism of action of antibiotic	Resistance observed (Y/N)	Test organisms inhibited

Isolates tested	Resistant (%)	Producers tested (number)	Resistant (%)

Interpretations and conclusions:

Notes:

Don't forget to update your entry and include your data in the Small World Initiative Soil Sample Database: *www.smallworldinitiative.org/data*

Section 11: "Classic" versus "Modern"

Biological Classification

Humans make sense of themselves and the world around them by classifying things based on their shared characteristics, whether it is by their physical appearance, function, or origin. For example, classification provides a shorthand for differentiating plants with medicinal value from those that are poisonous and differentiating animals that walk on their toes from those that walk on their knuckles. Carl Linnaeus, the father of modern taxonomy, pioneered the classification of organisms based on shared physical characteristics. He meticulously grouped organisms into taxonomic ranks and set the foundation for naming them, using a binomial containing the genus and species designation. Charles Darwin, on the other hand, championed the principles of common descent and paved the way for the classification of organisms based on their evolutionary relatedness. Whether it is looking at morphology or genetic similarity, each system of classification reflects different patterns of evolution and adaptation to environments, distribution in time and space, or utility to humans.

Whatever classification system we employ, it is important to know the criteria used to differentiate things. The use of molecular phylogeny has become the standard for classifying bacteria based on their genetic relatedness, but this is usually supported by morphological and biochemical characterization techniques as discussed in Section 8. To classify and identify bacteria, microbiologists assess many features, such as the structure or function of key biomolecules; the shape, size, or staining pattern of the cells; the type of metabolism; or DNA sequence composition.

In this section, we will describe some of the most common biochemical characterization methods, which are used in clinical diagnostic labs to identify bacterial pathogens isolated from patients. They are also applied in research labs to establish taxonomic and phylogenetic relationships, providing a better understanding of shared characteristics, evolution, and adaptation to natural environments than any single method alone.

The Diagnostics Lab

When it comes to diagnosing and treating patients, pathogen identification must be fast, reliable, and low cost, whenever possible. Classical methods of identification are based on fundamental microbiological principles about how bacteria respond to certain changes to their environment. For example, changing the chemical or nutrient composition of a growth medium affects how bacteria grow or what chemicals they produce. To exploit these changes, two types of specialized media are used – **selective media**, which support the growth of some species and not others, and **differential media**, which differentiate species by visible characteristics.

In hospitals, the use of selective media is a widespread method of identifying human pathogens. Bacteria may be isolated from bodily fluids (e.g., urine or blood), abscesses, or other areas of infection in the patient's body. These samples are streaked out on specialized media that accomplish different objectives. To identify methicillin-resistant bacteria present in a sample, we can formulate a selective medium containing methicillin, which will inhibit the growth of all susceptible bacteria but not the resistant ones – a simple process of elimination. Selective media may also lack an essential amino acid, which would inhibit bacteria unable to synthesize that nutrient. Differential media, on the other hand, will help distinguish groups of bacteria through changes in appearance of the organism or the medium itself, usually in response to differences in biochemical pathways. Researchers and clinical personnel use these visual cues to assign phenotypes and chemical reactions associated with known bacteria, pathogenic or not.

Specialized Media and Enzymology

As described in Section 8, Gram staining allows us to assign bacteria to one of two large groups of classification: Gram-negative or Gram-positive. Other tests do this while conveying even more information about the microbe's biochemistry. MacConkey agar is a specialized medium that differentiates between Gram-negative bacteria, especially those that colonize the human gastrointestinal (GI) tract. This medium inhibits the growth of Gram-positive bacteria by disrupting their cell walls with crystal violet and bile salts infused in the medium. Many Gram-negative bacteria, such as *Escherichia coli*, thrive in the GI tract as part of our natural gut flora along with many specialized Gram-positive bacteria. Other Gram-negative bacteria, such as *Salmonella* and *Shigella*, are notorious pathogens that can cause food poisoning and even death. To differentiate between these bacteria, MacConkey agar allows us to deduce information about their ability to ferment carbohydrates. A pH indicator in the medium changes the appearance of cells producing acid, as a by-product of fermentation, from their original color to pink/red. *E. coli* ferments the lactose present in the medium and releases acid, making colonies and the surrounding agar appear red in the presence of a pH indicator. Conversely, *Salmonella* and *Shigella* do not ferment lactose and maintain a neutral pH, making colonies display their typical white or tan color (Wessner, et al., p. 176). MacConkey agar is therefore both selective and differential, revealing information about the cell wall composition and ability to ferment lactose.

Another method to differentiate enteric bacteria based on their ability to metabolize different compounds is the triple sugar iron (TSI) test. TSI medium, which consists of solidified agar in a slanted test tube, supports classification of bacteria based on their ability to ferment different carbohydrates (glucose, sucrose, and lactose), to produce H_2S (hydrogen sulfide, a by-product of bacterial anaerobic digestion), and to grow in the presence or absence of oxygen (ASM Microbe Library). In this method, bacteria are stabbed into the agar, where they begin to metabolize sugars under aerobic conditions at the surface of the agar or anaerobic conditions at the butt of the tube. A pH indicator turns the medium from red to yellow in response to acid as a by-product of fermentation. For example, a lactose fermenter like *Escherichia* or *Klebsiella* will continue to lower the pH long after glucose and sucrose have been depleted in the medium. Since they are both facultative anaerobes, they will ferment sugar both in the presence and absence of oxygen, making the whole tube appear yellow. In contrast, *Citrobacter* and *Salmonella* will only ferment carbohydrates under anaerobic conditions and release H_2S. Therefore, only the butt of the tube will appear yellow, and black precipitate will form from the reaction of H_2S with ferric ions in the medium (Wessner et al., p. 175) (ASM Microbe Library).

Similarly, the starch agar test differentiates between bacteria that hydrolyze starch, a branched polymer of glucose units, and bacteria that do not. For this method, bacteria are grown on starch agar. When colonies become visible, the plate is flooded with iodine, which is normally red but turns blue when it complexes with starch, serving as an effective indicator for the presence or absence of starch molecules. A starch hydrolyzer like *Bacillus subtilis* will secrete amylase, which breaks down the surrounding starch to glucose. Upon flooding the colonies, the medium surrounding the colonies appears red in the absence of starch, which has been broken down by the amylase-positive bacteria. The rest of the plate will appear a dark shade of blue where the starch is still present. *Streptococcus* and *Staphylococcus* are both starch negative and can be used as controls.

By testing a bacterium's ability to metabolize different compounds, we are indirectly screening for the presence of key enzymes that are unique to certain taxonomic groups of bacteria. Bacteria are equipped to survive in distinct environments where different carbon and energy sources are available. They are also equipped to deal with a variety of mechanical, chemical, and environmental conditions that threaten their existence. For example, hydrogen peroxide (H_2O_2) is a strong oxidizing agent that rapidly kills susceptible cells and is employed by many organisms to protect against infectious bacteria. H_2O_2 is also used as an antiseptic applied on cuts or wounds on the skin. Nevertheless, many bacteria have evolved a mechanism to counteract H_2O_2 with the enzyme catalase. *Staphylococcus* bacteria, like those that colonize our skin, and *Bacillus*, which are commonly found in the soil, both test positive for the presence of this enzyme. Testing positive for catalase is made evident by exposing target bacteria to a 3% H_2O_2 solution and observing for effervescence. The reaction between catalase and H_2O_2 produces water and oxygen gas.

$$2H_2O_2 + \text{catalase} \rightarrow 2H_2O + O_2$$

When dealing with common or well-studied bacteria, these classical biochemistry-based tests can give us great information about our bacterium to narrow down the search to a specific class or family of bacteria. Diagnostic labs with well-developed identification keys can use these methods to type pathogens down to several genera and figure out a line of treatment for patients. However, to identify a bacterium down to the genus or species level, or when dealing with a poorly studied bacterium, sequencing technology is normally necessary.

Classic or Modern Approach

Over the past two decades, sequencing technologies have become faster, more reliable, and cheaper, leading to the exponential increase of sequenced genomes available in online repositories like GenBank and other databases. 16S rRNA gene sequencing has therefore become a useful method for identifying bacteria down to the genus level, and more specific primers can help us identify their species or particular strain. Knowing that a bacterium's 16S rRNA gene sequence has a 97% or higher similarity with a known species provides us information about an organism of interest and what phenotypes to expect. As we indicated in Section 8, researchers usually combine morphological, biochemical, and molecular analyses to provide a complete picture of the identity of an unknown organism. Results may bring to light discrepancies that may indicate we are dealing with a new strain or a variant of a known species. Whatever the case, coupling knowledge of a bacterium's phylogenetic background with morphology and biochemical information acquired through classical biochemistry-based methods allows us to draw a comprehensive picture of our isolates and acquire new insight into their cellular and molecular processes.

References

ASM Microbe Library. Laboratory Protocols. <http://www.asmscience.org/content/education/protocol> Date accessed: 21 November 2016.

Fox, A. Culture and Identification of Infectious Agents. Bacteriol Microbiol Immunol, On-Line: University of South Carolina School of Medicine <http://www.microbiologybook.org/fox/culture.htm> Date accessed: 21 November 2016.

Wessner, D. R., Dupont, C., & Charles, T. (2013) *Microbiology*.

Experiment 11: Conduct biochemical characterization of your isolates

Biological Questions:
- Now that you know the genus of your isolate, what else do you want to know about your isolates?
- Is our new biochemical characterization information consistent with previous (molecular and morphological) characterization data?

- Note: Reproduce the following prompts for every biochemical test done. -

Background:

Objective:

Biochemical test:

Procedure:

Results:

Interpretation:

Is this consistent with what you know about your isolate(s)?

Conclusions:

Notes:

Don't forget to update your entry and include your data in the Small World Initiative Soil Sample Database: *www.smallworldinitiative.org/data*

Section 12: Bacteria in Context

"Good" versus "Bad" Bacteria

The popular belief that all bacteria are "germs," which the Merriam-Webster's Dictionary defines as "microorganisms causing disease," has led to great efforts to eradicate bacteria from our lives with stringent sanitary and hygienic measures. Conversely, the food industry has marketed "good bacteria," or probiotics in fermented products, such as the "live and active culture" label on yogurts. This dichotomy has led to the notion that, in general, bacteria cannot be trusted but can have beneficial effects if consumed from the right packages. However, the notion of discretely "good" and "bad" bacteria is misleading. The truth is that most bacteria are harmless and are essential components of Earth's ecosystems and individual organisms. From birth, bacteria colonize our skin and guts, enhance our immune systems, and enrich our diets with nutrients that would otherwise be inaccessible to us as humans. The interdependence between bacteria and other organisms is not coincidental but is the product of a long history of coevolution and interspecies interactions.

Symbiotic Relationships

Relationships define the way we, humans, interact with each other. They define how we communicate, the way we feel toward one another, the agreement and level of commitment we hold, and the norms that dictate those interactions. They can last a short period of time or a lifetime, and they often lay a foundation for those same relationships in future generations. As social beings, and as living things, we are fundamentally interconnected and interdependent.

Symbiosis is a long-term, intimate relationship between two or more species (Wessner et al., p. 563). Like all relationships, symbioses may serve a variety of purposes for each of its participating members, whether it is receiving essential nutrients, providing shelter and protection, or disseminating progeny. These relationships often fall in a continuum between beneficial and harmful for one species versus the other (p. 563). On one end of the spectrum, a **mutualistic** relationship defines an interaction in which both species benefit. For example, herbivores rely on their gut bacteria to break down cellulose, and the gut bacteria in return are provided a habitat and a steady food supply. At the other end of the spectrum, a **parasitic** relationship defines an interaction where one species benefits and the other is harmed. Bacteria that have observable or measureable effects on their hosts may be mutualistic, parasitic, or fall anywhere in between.

Residing On or Inside Another Organism

Symbioses are not only defined by their effects (beneficial versus harmful) on the host, but also by their location in relationship to the host. The species involved in a symbiotic relationship are known as **symbionts**. **Ectosymbionts** reside on the surface of their host while **endosymbionts** reside in the tissues or within the cells of their host (Wessner et al., p. 563).

Most scientists now agree that eukaryotic cells are the product of a form of endosymbiosis. When biologist Lynn Margulis published a paper supporting the **endosymbiotic theory**, many scientists were quick to reject the idea that mitochondria and chloroplasts were once "free-living prokaryotic cells" engulfed by the early eukaryotic cells (Sagan, 1967). Today, molecular and genetic evidence supported by 16S rRNA sequencing of mitochondrial and chloroplast DNA indicates that these organelles may have originated from alpha-proteobacteria and cyanobacteria, respectively. The process of symbiosis was perhaps the single most important event in the evolution of complex organisms.

Figure 12-1. A mealybug feeding on sap.

Photo source:

<http://schaechter.asmblog.org/schaechter/2011/09/a-bug-in-a-bug-in-a-bug.html> Date accessed: 2 November 2013.

Figure 12-2. A leaf-cutting worker ant covered by the ectosymbiont *Streptomyces*. Leaf-cutting ants rely on the antibiotics produced by *Streptomyces* species to keep their "fungus farms" parasite-free.

Photo source:

<http://scienceblogs.com/notrocketscience/leafcutter-ants-rely-on-bacteria-to-fertilise-their-fungus-g/> Date accessed: 17 July 2014.

In the long term, some symbiotic relationships irreversibly alter host physiology, biochemistry, and genetics. The human genome with 21,000 protein-coding genes and the *E. coli* genome with just over 4,000 are both enormous in comparison with a bacterium entrenched in a three-way symbiosis. The bacterium *Candidatus Tremblaya princeps* contains 120 protein-coding genes, an unprecedentedly low number for any living organism. *Tremblaya*, an endosymbiont of the mealybug, synthesizes vitamins and amino acids from the sap consumed by its host in a mutually beneficial relationship. Yet *Tremblaya* is itself dependent on its own endosymbiont, the gamma-proteobacterium *Moranella*, whose genome is significantly larger, to synthesize proteins that are not encoded in *Tremblayas*'s minimalist genome

(Husnik et al., 2013). The interdependence displayed in this three-way symbiosis has meticulously divided labor between these organisms, all in the safety and steady food supply of the mealybug host (Figure 12-1).

Streptomyces, which have some of the largest bacterial genomes and produce most commercially and clinically used antibiotics, are also involved in symbiotic relationships thanks to their bioactivity against pathogens. Leaf-cutting ants rely on antibiotic producers like *Streptomyces* to protect their food from microbial infection. These so-called farming ants cultivate the fungus *Leucoagaricus* for food, which is prone to infection by yet another fungus called *Escovopsis* (Seipke et al., 2011; Haeder, Wirth, Herz, & Spiteller, 2009). *Streptomyces* live on the ants' exoskeletons as an ectosymbiont and produce antibiotics that specifically inhibit *Escovopsis* (Seipke et al., 2011). This protects the ants' cultivar fungus as their source of sustenance and provides shelter for the antibiotic producers living on them (Figure 12-2).

Plants and Microbes

Anywhere you look on the planet, plants interact with microbes in the soil, on their surfaces, and even living within their tissues. A few of these interactions are parasitic and are the cause for great loss in agriculture. Like the *Escovopsis* fungus threatening the crops of leaf-cutting ants, species of the eukaryotic microorganism *Pythium* attack the root tips of plants. Almost all plants are susceptible to *Pythium*, which, under the right conditions and with no competition, can spread very quickly and ravage fields with root rot (Moorman, 2013). The use of biological control agents, such as bacteria that enhance crop growth or inhibit plant disease, has been purposely applied in agriculture to restore the balance. Thus, our dependence on bacteria for our food source is tightly intertwined with the practices of modern agriculture.

Bacteria have been used for millennia to enhance crop nutrition. Nitrogen gas (N_2) constitutes roughly 80% of Earth's atmosphere. This abundant form of nitrogen, which is an essential component of amino acids and nucleotides, is inaccessible for the vast majority of organisms because of the ultra-stable triple bond between N atoms in N_2. Genes encoding nitrogenase, the enzyme that converts N_2 from the atmosphere to NH_4^+ (ammonium), have only been found in Bacteria and Archaea (Wessner et al., p. 474). The conversion of nitrogen gas into ammonium is known as **nitrogen fixation**, an important part of the nitrogen cycle. Ammonium and its deprotonated form, ammonia (NH_3), can then be assimilated by many organisms, like plants, into essential biological molecules (Figure 12-3).

Leguminous plants (e.g., beans, peanuts, and peas), which are protein rich, have a high demand for nitrogen and have evolved living quarters for nitrogen-fixing bacteria. Bacteria that live in the soil with a plant host and fix nitrogen are collectively known as **rhizobia**. The legumes form **root nodules** that house the rhizobia in a perfect partnership. The pea plant secretes a chemical signal that invites *Rhizobium* to its root hairs (elongated cells on the surface of the root), and once the microbe-plant contact occurs, the root hair curls around the bacteria, enveloping them inside the root cell (Needham, 2000). The rhizobia spread into the root cortex through a plant structure called an infection thread, and in the cortex, the bacteria lose their cell walls as they make their home within plant cells and become nitrogen-fixing bacteroids. The root nodule provides an anaerobic environment for nitrogenase activity.

In order to provide oxygen (O_2) for other reactions without interfering with nitrogen fixation, plants produce the hemeprotein leghemoglobin, which carries oxygen to the cells while simultaneously sequestering it away from nitrogenase (Wessner et al., p. 566). This interdependence between legumes and rhizobia demonstrates a shared evolutionary history.

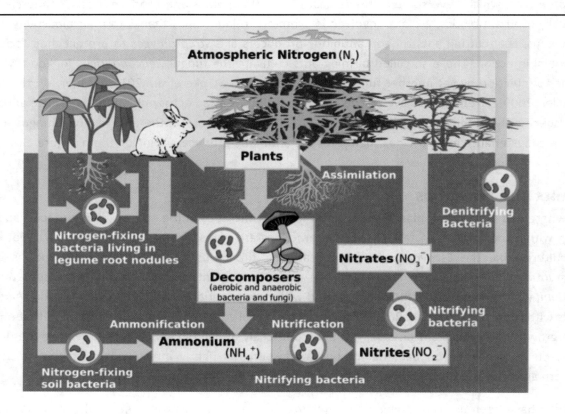

Figure 12-3. Schematic of nitrogen cycle. Bacteria play a crucial role in the fixing nitrogen and making it usable for plants. Photo source: commons.wikimedia.org.

Microbes and Us

Microbes not only make up most of the cells and DNA inside and on our bodies, but also play important roles in our digestive system, immunity, and probably even behavior. Whether we acquire them from things we touch, from yogurt or other fermented products, or from each other or other species, categorizing them as either "good" or "bad" is not straightforward. The Human Microbiome Project, an initiative launched by the U.S. National Institutes of Health, seeks to characterize all the entities that make up the **human microbiome**, or collection of microorganisms in our bodies. Articles challenging traditional views of microbes and urging us to "tend" our microbial flora with "good" bacteria-promoting diets and even microbiota transplants (Zimmer, 2012) permeate the media. Nevertheless, bacteria that can enrich our nutrition and prevent pathogenic bacteria from colonizing the gut epithelium can be closely related to the bacteria that cause of food poisoning and lead to massive product recalls. That is because bacteria, like all organisms, exist in their current state in context. *E. coli* in the intestine behaves very differently from *E. coli* in the bloodstream, and so does its gene expression machinery. Microbes in a **consortium**, or a collection of symbiotic species in a microbial community, are kept in check by neighboring organisms but display different phenotypes in isolation. This creates a challenge when studying microbes outside of their context, whether that is a set of abiotic conditions or the inside of mealybug.

Final Note

The current focus in microbiology has shifted from studying microbes in isolation, i.e., in single-species cultures, to studying microbes in mixed-species communities and other forms of microbe-microbe associations. As we have seen, microbes are shaped by their context – the microbes that surround them and their physical environment – and we can learn far more about their biology by observing their responses to these interactions than by studying them only in isolation. (We also know from Section 1 that microbes have also shaped their surroundings.) Bacteria grow and look very different in the lab than they do in the soil, and most of the time (~99%), they are not culturable under standard laboratory conditions; we simply do not understand the complexity of their requirements well enough to design culture conditions that suit them.

In our antibiotic activity assays, we were only expecting one type of interaction: antagonism, which results in a clear zone of inhibition. Yet in some cases, you may have noticed that your tester strain or bacterial isolate grew slightly differently or displayed a different morphology in the presence of the other. Maybe one organism enhances the other's growth or cooperates to access resources. These interactions could be the focus of a whole other course in microbiology research or someone's entire life's work on research. Just search "microbial communities" or "mixed-species" or "biofilms" on your search engine, and the wealth of up-and-coming research you find will be tremendous!

It is important to recognize that our approach to studying microbes has been very targeted, and that just as microbes are abundant and diverse, so are the possibilities of research. As you go on to pursue the chemical structure of your antibiotic or study its spectrum and mechanism of action in more detail, keep in mind that each bacterium contains a wealth of information, which grows as you study it in the context of other organisms or other variables. You have already gotten a strong foundation to talk about your microbes, learn more about them in the literature, and design some final experiments. The insights you have gathered about them are the product of your interactions with the organism, and in many ways, *you* have become their context. This is the nature of research. Our experiences leave an indelible mark in the world, and with this research, you have left yours.

References

Haeder, S., Wirth, R., Herz, H., & Spiteller, D. (2009). Candicidin-producing *Streptomyces* support leaf-cutting ants to protect their fungus garden against the pathogenic fungus *Escovopsis*. Proc Natl Acad Sci U S A, 106:4742-4746.

Husnik, F., Nikoh, N., Koga, R., Ross, L., Duncan, R. P., Fujie, M., Tanaka, M., Satoh, N., Bachtrog, D., Wilson, A. C., von Dohlen, D. D., Fukatsu, T., & McCutcheon, J. P. (2013). Horizontal gene transfer from diverse bacteria to an insect genome enables a tripartite nested mealybug symbiosis. Cell, 153(7):1567-1578. doi: 10.1016/j.cell.2013.05.040.

Moorman, G. W. (2013). Plants & Pests: Pythium. Penn State College of Agricultural Sciences. http://extension.psu.edu/pests/plant-diseases/all-fact-sheets/pythium

Needham, C. (2000). *Intimate Strangers: Unseen Life on Earth*. Washington, DC: ASM Press.

Sagan, L. (1967). On the origin of mitosing cells. *J Theor Biol*, 14:255-274.

Seipke, R. F., Barke, J., Brearley, C., Hill, L., Yu, D. W., Goss, R. J. M., & Hutchings, M. I. (2011). A single *Streptomyces* symbiont makes multiple antifungals to support the fungus farming ant *Acromyrmex octospinosus*. *PLoS ONE*, 6:e22028. doi: 10.1371/journal.pone.0022028.

Wessner, D. R., Dupont, C., & Charles, T. (2013) *Microbiology*.

Zimmer, C. Tending the Body's Microbial Garden. The New York Times. June 18, 2012. http://www.nytimes.com/2012/06/19/science/studies-of-human-microbiome-yield-new-insights.html?_r=0

Experiment 12: Assess your isolate's activity against eukaryotes, potential use as biological control, and ecological relationships with other organisms

Biological Questions:
- Could we use the antibiotics produced by our isolates to treat bacterial infections in humans? Why or why not?
- How do our antibiotic-producing isolates interact with plants and other organisms?
- Could we use the antibiotic-producing organism as a biological control agent in our crops? Against what disease?

Isolate's interactions with plants:

Hypothesis and rationale:

Experimental design and protocols used:

Controls and treatments:

Observations:

Interpretations and conclusions:

Isolate's effect on plant pathogens, e.g., *Pythium*:

Hypothesis and rationale:

Experimental design and protocols used:

Controls and treatments:

Observations:

Interpretations and conclusions:

Design experiment to assess other ecological relationships:

Don't forget to update your entry and include your data in the Small World Initiative Soil Sample Database: *www.smallworldinitiative.org/data*

Future Directions

Moving Forward from Bacterial Isolate to Molecules

The study of natural products for human benefit is a very old science that has its roots in herbal remedies, pigments and dyes, and volatile perfumery oils. Since soil microorganisms have traditionally been a good source of antibiotics, the end goal of the Small World Initiative program is to isolate the compounds that are producing the zones of inhibition that were observed during the initial stages of the course. At some point during the course, cultures of the interesting organisms will be grown and extracted with a solvent to produce a crude extract. These crude extracts are typically complex mixtures of chemicals. There are three main things that are required to go from a microbial isolate to a biologically active molecule, through a process called bioassay-guided isolation:

1. Biological Assay

2. Purification Techniques

3. Structure Determination Techniques

First, a biological assay is required so the activity can be followed as the purification techniques are used to isolate the active molecule away from other components. Once a pure molecule is obtained, techniques that can identify the molecule due to unique characteristics are used to determine its chemical structure.

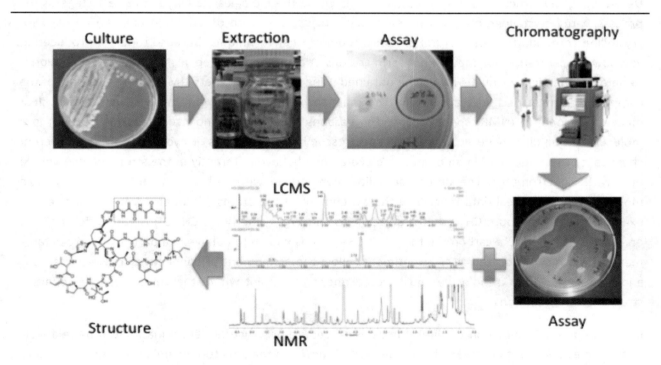

Figure 13-1. Bioassay-guided isolation of thiostrepton from a *Streptomyces* sp. during CHEM167 Microbes to Molecules II by undergraduate Kira Garry.

Bioassay-guided isolation typically involves expensive equipment, is time intensive, and often leads to known compounds. So before an extract goes through this process, it needs to go through a de-replication procedure. This procedure allows identification of extracts that contain commonly re-isolated compounds and allows the researcher to prioritize extracts containing novel compounds. Liquid chromatography/mass spectrometry (LC/MS) along with statistical analysis and biological assays that provide mode of action information further characterize the compound. Once an extract has been prioritized for further work, it will undergo bioassay-guided isolation. A simple example of this is shown in Figure 13-1, which summarizes the isolation of thiostrepton from a *Streptomyces* sp. during a Small World Initiative course (Microbes to Molecules II – CHEM167 at Yale University by Kira Garry).

1. Biological Assay

A biological assay is required before purification starts, so the activity can be followed at each step.

2. Purification Techniques

The purification of crude extracts is done using various techniques that can be described as liquid chromatography (LC). Highly automated and easy-to-use LC systems are now common in chemistry research laboratories that allow for fast and relatively cheap purification of mixtures. HPLC (high performance LC) systems are also available where the purification to a single compound is difficult.

3. Structure Determination Techniques

Determining the structure of the molecule that is giving the biological activity is the next stage of the process. X-ray crystallography, which essentially provides a picture of the molecule, can be used for crystalline compounds. Most natural products require other techniques because they are produced at very low concentrations or they do not form crystals. A common first step in structure determination is to obtain a chemical formula. This can be obtained using mass spectrometry (MS) where the mass of the compound is measured very accurately. The main technique used to determine structure is nuclear magnetic resonance (NMR) spectroscopy. The carbons (^{13}C isotope) and hydrogens (^{1}H isotope) in a molecule can be directly detected by NMR spectroscopy. When carbons or hydrogens are in a different chemical environment within an organic molecule, they behave differently in the strong magnetic field of a NMR spectrometer. The differences allow comparison with carbons and hydrogens in known molecules and historical data that allow the assignment of the atoms within an organic molecule. For example, a methyl group (CH_3^-) that is adjacent to an oxygen (methoxy; CH_3-O-) is very different from one that is attached to a carbon (methyl; CH3-CH_2-) and is known to behave in a particularly predictable manner. More sophisticated NMR experiments allow the assignment of connectivity between carbons and hydrogens within a molecule and have advanced to a point where they often provide definitive structure determinations.

If the compound is known in the literature, this procedure of structure determination can be relatively fast and may take days or weeks. If the compound is new and the structure is similar but not identical to molecules already in the literature, then the process may take weeks to months depending on the complexity of the molecule. In complicated cases, where the carbon backbone has not been observed before, the structure of the novel compound may take months to unravel, particularly if issues of stereochemistry are involved. The mode of action is a key area of interest when novel compounds are isolated since the overall goal of the Small World Initiative is to isolate new and novel compounds from environmental isolates. If novel molecules can be identified with new modes of action, this work could have true impact in the area of drug discovery and treatment of infectious disease.

Concluding Remarks

Think about how far you have come in only a few weeks. You have learned about the global antibiotic crisis, you have learned that soil is not just "dirt," you have isolated bacteria from your own soil samples, and you have applied the scientific method to investigate these samples. Throughout this time, you have learned how to communicate with your peers in your classroom and around the world, and you have shared your lab results with them. You are on your way to becoming an active partner in the educational mission of your campus and a lifelong learner.

Furthermore, you have played an important role on what the United Nations has called "the greatest and most urgent global risk." While local, national, and global actions are required to solve the antibiotic crisis, individuals can have an impact. Going forward, consider simple things you can do to stop the misuse of antibiotics and reduce the spread of infections, including washing your hands, supporting companies that adopt safe antibiotic-use policies, getting vaccinated, and not demanding antibiotics when you have a viral infection like a cold or flu. Remember, in the United States, consumer demand led to nine of the largest food chains adopting new sourcing policies that require antibiotic-free meat, which have prompted changes in agricultural practices. It is important for you to understand your power as an individual and a consumer.

While we are running out of time to deal with the public health emergency of antibiotic resistance, it is not too late if we respond effectively with global collaboration. Through your research, you have already been part of a global initiative to crowdsource antibiotic discovery through the efforts of thousands of student researchers conducting mass-scale fundamental biological discovery.

Even though antimicrobial resistance has significant global consequences, humans have the ingenuity to solve this problem...if we act. We hope that everyone in the Small World Initiative will recognize that, together, we can make a difference.